David Kent
Keith Pledger
Roy Woodward

HEINEM... MATHEM...

Foundation Course

These are the different types of pages and symbols used in this book:

Shape: volume **24**

These pages develop mathematical skills, concepts and facts in a wide variety of realistic contexts.

Problem solving **34**

These pages develop mathematical problem-solving skills.

▶ **Do Worksheet 1**

This shows you when you need to use a Worksheet.

● **Remember**

This is a reminder of the key information essential for the work of the pages.

■ **Investigation**

Investigations enhance the work of the page by providing additional opportunities to develop problem-solving skills.

Heinemann

Contents

Part 1

Part 2

Part 4

Around the centre

Naomi is captain of the school hockey team.

Range

Naomi's team has played 10 matches. They scored these goals in each of the matches

3, 1, 3, 0, 2, 4, 3, 0, 1, 3

The highest number of goals they scored was 4
The lowest number of goals they scored was 0
The difference between the highest and lowest was

4 − 0 = 4

This is called the **range** of the number of goals scored.

Mean

The **mean** number of goals scored per match is

$$\frac{3 + 1 + 3 + 0 + 2 + 4 + 3 + 0 + 1 + 3}{10} = 2\cdot0$$

The mean number of goals is always

the total number of goals scored
the number of matches played

I In the ten matches Naomi's team had these numbers of goals scored against them.

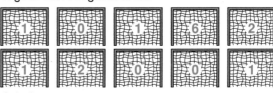

Calculate:

(a) the range of the goals scored against them

(b) the mean of the number of goals scored against them.

Mode

In their 10 matches Naomi's team scored

0 goals on 2 occasions
1 goal on 2 occasions
2 goals on 1 occasion
3 goals on 4 occasions
4 goals on 1 occasion.

The number of goals they scored on the **most** occasions was 3. 3 is the **mode** (or **modal number**) of the number of goals they scored.

2 What was the mode of the number of goals scored against Naomi's team?

Median

Naomi lists the goals they scored in order, from lowest to highest. This gives

0, 0, 1, 1, 2, 3, 3, 3, 3, 4

Because there is an even number of numbers, the two numbers in the middle of this list are either 2 or 3. Naomi adds these together and divides by 2.

$$\frac{2+3}{2} = 2\frac{1}{2} \qquad \text{(or 2·5)}$$

This number is the **median**.

3 Find the median of the number of goals scored against Naomi's team.

4 In an ice-skating competition the 8 judges award the following marks

5·4	5·6	5·6	5·7
5·5	5·7	5·8	5·6

For these marks calculate:

(a) the range   **(b)** the mean
(c) the mode   **(d)** the median.

Sometimes there may be an **odd** number of scores. This does not affect how you find the range, mean or mode, but it makes finding the median easier.

5 Sally does 11 pieces of homework for geography. Her marks are 7, 6, 7, 8, 8, 7, 5, 6, 6, 9, 9
For her marks find:

(a) the range   **(b)** the mean
(c) the mode   **(d)** the median.

6 The ages of 22 people are given in this table.

Number of people	5	5	5	6	1
Age in years	14	15	16	17	18

For those ages find:

(a) the range   **(b)** the mean
(c) the mode   **(d)** the median.
Be careful in **(b)**, the mean is not
(14 + 15 + 16 + 17 + 18) ÷ 5

Many times quicker

1 Find:

(a) 17×10 (b) 10×26 (c) 141×10

(d) 17×20 (e) 135×20 (f) 18×30

(g) 21×100 (h) 34×100 (i) 14×200

(j) 122×200 (k) 211×300 (l) 234×400

Pam buys 12 packets of nails. Each packet contains 64 nails, how many nails does she have altogether?

$12 \times 64 = ?$

$$
\begin{array}{ll}
10 \times 64 = 640 & \quad\text{or}\quad & 10 \times 64 = 640 \\
1 \times 64 = 64 & & 2 \times 64 = 128 \\
1 \times 64 = 64 & & \overline{12 \times 64 = 768} \\
\overline{12 \times 64 = 768} &
\end{array}
$$

Pam has 768 nails.

2 How many nails will there be in 24 packets?

3 Find:

(a) 12×41 (b) 13×35 (c) 14×82

(d) 15×36 (e) 16×67 (f) 15×124

Jonathan was asked to work out 18×44. This is how he did it.

$18 \times 44 = ?$

$$
\begin{array}{ll}
10 \times 44 = 440 & \\
5 \times 44 = 220 & \text{(half of } 10 \times 44\text{)} \\
1 \times 44 = 44 & \\
1 \times 44 = 44 & \\
1 \times 44 = 44 & \\
\overline{18 \times 44 = 792} &
\end{array}
$$

4 Try to use Jonathan's way to answer these questions.

(a) 15×32 (b) 15×48 (c) 16×86

(d) 18×25 (e) 17×17 (f) 19×62

5 Can you suggest Braynbox's method for working out 19×62?

I've found an even quicker method of multiplication. It uses multiplying by 10 and then subtraction.

Sharma buys 34 boxes of Christmas cards to sell in her shop. Each box contains 24 cards. How many Christmas cards does she buy altogether?

$34 \times 24 = ?$

$$
\begin{array}{ll}
10 \times 24 = 240 & \quad\text{or}\quad & 30 \times 24 = 720 \\
10 \times 24 = 240 & & 4 \times 24 = 96 \\
10 \times 24 = 240 & & \overline{34 \times 24 = 816} \\
1 \times 12 = 24 & \\
1 \times 24 = 24 & \\
1 \times 24 = 24 & \\
1 \times 24 = 24 & \\
\overline{34 \times 24 = 816} &
\end{array}
$$

Sharma has 816 Christmas cards.

6 How many Christmas cards will there be in 25 boxes?

7 Find:

(a) 13×26 (b) 14×39 (c) 15×44

(d) 21×64 (e) 24×18 (f) 42×53

(g) 36×72 (h) 59×21 (i) 98×81

For his homework Paul is asked to find out how many hours there are in 132 days. To find the answer he knows that he must multiply 132 by 24.

$132 \times 24 = ?$

$$
\begin{array}{ll}
100 \times 24 = 2400 & \quad\text{or}\quad & 100 \times 24 = 2400 \\
10 \times 24 = 240 & & 30 \times 24 = 720 \\
10 \times 24 = 240 & & 2 \times 24 = 48 \\
10 \times 24 = 240 & & \overline{132 \times 24 = 3168} \\
1 \times 24 = 24 & \\
1 \times 24 = 24 & \\
\overline{132 \times 24 = 3168} &
\end{array}
$$

There are 3168 hours in 132 days.

8 How many hours are there in 126 days?

9 Find:

(a) 114×45 (b) 132×49

(c) 145×31 (d) 213×82

(e) 312×64 (f) 362×48

(g) 485×52 (h) 634×75

(i) 883×86 (j) 234×447

A prize of £168 was shared equally between 12 people.
How much did each person get?
This method uses multiplication to solve the problem.

168 ÷ 12

		Total	
try	10 × 12 = 120	120	(too small)
try	2 × 12 = 24	144	(still too small)
try	2 × 12 = 24	168	(correct answer)
	14 × 12 = 168		

Since   14 × 12 = 168
        168 ÷ 12 = 14

Each person gets £14.

1 How much would each person have received if the prize had been £204?

2 Work out:
   (a) 143 ÷ 11   (b) 195 ÷ 13
   (c) 238 ÷ 14   (d) 216 ÷ 12
   (e) 323 ÷ 19   (f) 240 ÷ 15

Mr Green has 667 counters and wants to divide them equally between his class of 29 students. How many does each student get?
The problem is 667 ÷ 29.
This is how Mr Green solves the problem.

		Total	
try	10 × 29 = 290	290	(much too small)
try	10 × 29 = 290	580	(still too small)
try	2 × 29 = 58	638	(still too small)
try	1 × 29 = 29	667	(correct)
	23 × 29 = 667		

Each student gets **23 counters**.

3 How many counters would each student get if Mr Green had 754 counters?

4 Find:
   (a) 224 ÷ 16   (b) 306 ÷ 18
   (c) 408 ÷ 17   (d) 364 ÷ 28
   (e) 372 ÷ 31   (f) 551 ÷ 29
   (g) 714 ÷ 42   (h) 1134 ÷ 63

Natasha has been asked to find the remainder when 371 is divided by 24. This is how Natasha solves her problem.

		Total	
try	10 × 24 = 240	240	(too small)
try	5 × 24 = 120	360	(too small)
try	1 × 24 = 24	384	(too big)
So	15 × 24 = 360	16 × 24 = 384	

The **remainder** must be 371 − 360 = **11**

5 Find the remainder when 427 is divided by 24.

6 Find the remainder when:
   (a) 145 ÷ 12   (b) 243 ÷ 21   (c) 243 ÷ 31
   (d) 315 ÷ 25   (e) 562 ÷ 32   (f) 535 ÷ 27
   (g) 642 ÷ 19   (h) 723 ÷ 43   (i) 799 ÷ 53
   (j) 856 ÷ 44   (k) 943 ÷ 64   (l) 999 ÷ 99

7 Leanne and Natasha go to a 24 hour charity disco. The DJ plays 17 records an hour. How many records were played altogether?

8 The storage tank of a petrol pump holds 13 064 litres of petrol. How many cars with fuel tanks that hold 23 litres can be filled from the pump?

9 An ocean liner sails 2045 km in 18 days. If it sailed 120 km for each of the first 17 days, how many kilometres did it sail on the last day?

10 Westdale School has 868 pupils and 28 classrooms. How many students are there in each class if each class has the same number of students?

11 The side of a rectangular wall has 27 rows of bricks and each row contains 136 bricks.
   Find:
   (a) the total number of bricks in the wall
   (b) the cost to build the wall if each brick costs 37p.

It's all the same to me

You need a calculator.

1 Copy these and find the next two equivalent fractions.

(a)

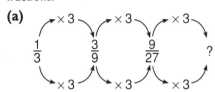

(b)

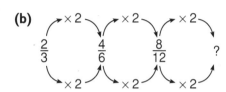

2 Multiply each fraction by the number shown to make 3 more equivalent fractions.

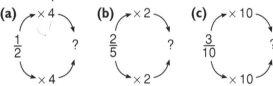

3 For each of these sets of equivalent fractions find the values of a and b.

(a) $\frac{1}{3} = \frac{2}{b} = \frac{a}{12}$ **(b)** $\frac{3}{4} = \frac{a}{12} = \frac{27}{b}$

(c) $\frac{a}{2} = \frac{5}{b} = \frac{10}{20}$ **(d)** $\frac{2}{a} = \frac{10}{25} = \frac{50}{b}$

Toni has been asked to find the equivalent fraction to $\frac{1}{2}$ which has a denominator of 100. She notices this number pattern

$$\frac{1}{2} = \frac{?}{100}$$

$\frac{1}{2} = \frac{?}{100}$ and completes it

$\frac{1}{2} = \frac{50}{100}$ with ×50 arrows

so $\frac{1}{2} = \frac{50}{100}$

4 Change these fractions into their equivalent fractions with a denominator of 100.

(a) $\frac{1}{2}$ **(b)** $\frac{1}{4}$ **(c)** $\frac{1}{5}$

(d) $\frac{3}{4}$ **(e)** $\frac{2}{5}$ **(f)** $\frac{3}{10}$

(g) $\frac{7}{20}$ **(h)** $\frac{9}{25}$ **(i)** $\frac{27}{50}$

$$\frac{1}{2} = 0 \cdot 5$$

These are also equivalent fractions. The 0·5 is the decimal fraction equivalent to $\frac{1}{2}$

To change a fraction into its decimal equivalent, divide the numerator by the denominator

$1 \div 2 = 0 \cdot 5$

5 Change these fractions into their equivalent decimal fractions.

(a) $\frac{3}{4}$ **(b)** $\frac{3}{5}$ **(c)** $\frac{7}{20}$

(d) $\frac{9}{25}$ **(e)** $\frac{1}{8}$ **(f)** $\frac{5}{8}$

(g) $\frac{1}{3}$ **(h)** $\frac{2}{9}$ **(i)** $\frac{5}{12}$

6 Sonja has to arrange these fractions in size, smallest first

$$\frac{3}{4} \qquad \frac{3}{5} \qquad \frac{7}{10}$$

(a) Find the equivalent fraction of each with a denominator of 20.

(b) Arrange them in size order, smallest first.

7 Arrange these fractions in size order, smallest first.

$$\frac{5}{6} \qquad \frac{7}{12} \qquad \frac{2}{3} \qquad \frac{3}{4}$$

1 Natasha works at the Safetysave Building Society. She sorts all the cheques the building society receives. At the end of the day Natasha puts all the cheques in order with the cheque for the smallest amount first. On Monday Safetysave receives cheques for:
£16·43, £45·54, £23·99, £4·90, 78p, £30
Write these amounts in order with the smallest first.

2 The next day Safetysave receives cheques for:
£12·34, £12·89, £12·43, £12·97, £12, £12·09
Write these amounts in order with the smallest first.

3 Charlie obtains these marks for his half term examinations.

Westdale School

Maths	32/40
English	38/50
French	21/25
German	17/20
Science	82/100

These marks can be changed into decimal fractions by dividing the numerator by the denominator.

Maths $\frac{32}{40}$, $32 \div 40 = 0·8$

(a) Rewrite all the subjects giving the results as a decimal fraction.

(b) Rewrite the results in size order with the best result first.

You need a calculator.

4 (a) Work out the answers to these questions:
$4·6 \times 2·5$
$2·4 \times 3·9$
$5·2 \times 3·1$
$7·3 \times 1·4$
$6·2 \times 2·1$
$12·5 \times 0·8$

(b) Write your answers in size order, with the smallest first.

5 Rewrite the questions in size order of their answers.
$3·6 \div 2·4$
$0·8 \div 0·6$
$6·2 \div 3·9$
$14·8 \div 9·3$
$132·7 \div 86·8$

6 Louise buys a packet of fig biscuits. The packet contains 15 biscuits. For a science project Louise had to weigh each biscuit.
The results were:

19·6 g	20·8 g	22·1 g
18·8 g	23·1 g	19·9 g
21·0 g	20·8 g	18·6 g
21·4 g	21·7 g	19·8 g
20·3 g	20·6 g	21·4 g

Copy and complete:

Interval	Tally	Frequency
18·0 to 18·9		
19·0 to 19·9		
20·0 to 20·9		
21·0 to 21·9		
22·0 to 22·9		
23·0 to 23·9		
	Total	15

7 This number has been attacked by Bertie the Blot. The clues should help you find the rest of the numbers.

Clue 1. The tens column is half of 6.

Clue 2. The units column is the square root of 16.

Clue 3. The 100ths column is the highest odd number on a normal 6 sided die.

Clue 4. The hundreds column is this question number.

Clue 5. The 10ths column can be seen.

Clue 6. The 1000ths column is the last digit of your age.

Write the number hidden under the ink blot.

8 Eight lengths of wood were measured and found to be
2 m 45 cm   2449 mm
248 cm   2·34 m
2·62 m   241 cm
2457 mm   2 m 57 cm
Write the lengths in size order, smallest first, all using the same unit of measurement.

That's only part of it

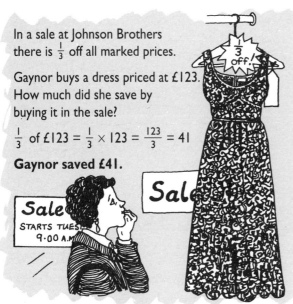

In a sale at Johnson Brothers there is $\frac{1}{3}$ off all marked prices.

Gaynor buys a dress priced at £123. How much did she save by buying it in the sale?

$$\frac{1}{3} \text{ of } £123 = \frac{1}{3} \times 123 = \frac{123}{3} = 41$$

Gaynor saved £41.

1 Find the saving by buying these goods from Johnson Brothers during their sale:

(a) a television set priced at £504
(b) an electric toaster priced at £24·30
(c) an electric kettle priced at £18·54
(d) a compact disc priced at £13·26
(e) a lawn mower priced at £304·35

2 Find:

(a) $\frac{1}{5}$ of 6·75 m   (b) $\frac{1}{4}$ of £16·72
(c) $\frac{2}{3}$ of 43·2 kg   (d) $\frac{2}{5}$ of 125 ml
(e) $\frac{5}{8}$ of 40 min   (f) $\frac{5}{12}$ of 180 g
(g) $\frac{3}{4}$ of 2 min   (h) $\frac{3}{5}$ of 2·45 cm

3 A vending machine sells 1968 drinks each week. The fractions sold are

$\frac{1}{4}$ tea $\frac{1}{8}$ chocolate

$\frac{1}{3}$ coffee $\frac{7}{24}$ koke

How many drinks of each type are sold?

4 Tom, Pat, Delroy and Marissa set out on a 36 km charity run. Tom completes $\frac{3}{4}$ of the run, Pat $\frac{5}{6}$ and Delroy $\frac{11}{12}$. Marissa completes the full course. Find:

(a) the total distance each person ran
(b) the total amount collected for charity if they were each given 45p for every kilometre run
(c) the fraction not completed by each runner.

5 Out of 712 students in year Y11, 178 decided to stay on in the 6th form.

(a) What fraction stayed on?
(b) What decimal fraction stayed on?
(c) What percentage stayed on?

6 In a box containing 80 oranges, 16 were bad.

(a) What fraction of the oranges were bad?
(b) What decimal fraction of the oranges were good?

7 During one week the post office found that of all letters posted

$\frac{1}{4}$ were being sent 2nd class, correctly addressed

$\frac{7}{10}$ were being sent 1st class, correctly addressed

The rest were incorrectly addressed.
If the number of letters received at the post office during the week was 46 820, find:

(a) the number of 1st and 2nd class correctly addressed letters posted
(b) the number of incorrectly addressed letters.

8 Hughie, the local electrician, rewires old houses. The cost to rewire a house is made up from

wire and trunking	$\frac{3}{80}$
switches and sockets	$\frac{17}{80}$
control unit	$\frac{1}{5}$
labour	$\frac{7}{40}$
profit	$\frac{3}{8}$

(a) How much is spent on each item for a house which cost £1680 to rewire?
(b) What percentage of the cost is the combined cost of the wire and trunking and switches and sockets?
(c) What is the decimal equivalent of Hughie's profit?

9 Jean, Derek and Tony inherit £3000 in total in a distant relative's will. Jean receives $\frac{1}{3}$, Derek $\frac{1}{4}$ and Tony the rest.

(a) How much does Jean receive?
(b) How much does Derek receive?
(c) What are the two decimal fraction equivalents to Jean's and Derek's shares?
(d) What, as a decimal fraction, was Tony's share?

1 Write these calculator displays to the nearest whole number.

(a) `3.47` (b) `19.8` (c) `0.89`

2 (a) Calculate the area of this square. Write the full calculator display.

(b) What is the area to the nearest whole number?

(c) What is the perimeter to the nearest whole number?

2·48 cm

Surjit has used her calculator to work out the answer to 12·13 × 1·661.
The full calculator display is

`20.14793`

She discards the last three digits and her calculator shows

`20.14 793`

She corrects her answer to

• 2 decimal places

20·15

1 2

or

• 4 significant figures

20·15
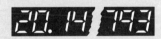
1 2 3 4

3 Write the answer to Surjit's question correct to:

(a) 3 decimal places

(b) 3 significant figures.

4 Write these numbers correct to the approximation given.

(a) 134·27 (1 dp) (b) 35·786 (2 sf)
(c) 0·67381 (4 dp) (d) 2745·6 (4 sf)
(e) 1·999 (2 dp) (f) 5·999 (1 sf)
(g) 17·9932 (3 dp) (h) 17·993 (2 sf)

36 182 people attended a pop concert held at Meadowhill Stadium. When this figure was reported in the *Meadowhill Messenger* it read

Meadowhill Messenger
36 000 attended a concert last night at

The number 36 182 had been written correct to 2 significant figures.

36 000
↑↑
1 2

It is important that zeros are included to give the correct place value to the first two digits.
The answer is 36 thousand not 36.

5 23 672 spectators watched Shimpling United beat Darbye County in the cup. Write the attendance correct to:

(a) 4 sig fig (b) 2 sig fig (c) 1 sig fig

6 These are the full results for a 3000 m steeplechase. Calculate the average speed of each runner correct to 3 significant figures.

Runner	Time (min)	Average speed (m/min)
Natasha	26·87	112
Leanne	26·32	
Gaynor	31·45	
Tony	25·70	
Suzanne	34·75	
Derek	31·89	
Andrew	25·56	

7 This conversion chart can be used to change pints to litres.

(a) Write 5 pints in litres correct to 2 decimal places.

(b) Write 18 pints in litres correct to 1 decimal place.

(c) Write 37 pints correct to 2 significant figures.

PINTS	LITRES
1	0·571
2	1·143
3	1·714
4	2·286
5	2·857
10	5·714
20	11·423

Percentages 1

1 Find:

(a) $240 \div 10$ (b) $430 \div 10$ (c) $580 \div 10$
(d) $324 \div 10$ (e) $743 \div 10$ (f) $101 \div 10$
(g) $72 \div 10$ (h) $56 \div 10$ (i) $45 \div 10$
(j) $460 \div 20$ (k) $82 \div 20$ (l) $360 \div 30$
(m) $24 \div 20$ (n) $44 \div 40$ (o) $35 \div 20$

2 Find:

(a) $260 \div 100$ (b) $450 \div 100$ (c) $342 \div 100$
(d) $89 \div 100$ (e) $440 \div 200$ (f) $60 \div 200$
(g) $14 \div 200$ (h) $330 \div 300$ (i) $250 \div 200$

3 Find $\frac{1}{10}$ of:

(a) £640 (b) £256 (c) £445
(d) £14 (e) £56 (f) £84
(g) £24·50 (h) £64·90 (i) £125·60

At Westdale School 43% of the pupils travel to school by bus. If 1800 pupils attend the school how many travel by bus?

First find: 10% of 1800 = 180 and
              1% of 1800   = 18

To find 43%
              40% of 1800 = 180 × 4 = 720
              3% of 1800   = 18 × 3 = 54
              43% of 1800 = 774

4 If 26% of the pupils at Westdale School are under the age of 13, find:

(a) how many students are under 13 years
(b) how many are 13 years or older.

5 21 000 spectators watched Shimpling United play their football match at home. If 32% of the crowd were away supporters find:

(a) the number of away supporters
(b) the number of home supporters
(c) the percentage of home supporters.

6 In her maths test Esther obtained 65% of the total marks.
Find her actual mark if the total mark was:

(a) 240 (b) 320 (c) 70

7 This table shows the percentage of boys and girls at Eastgrove School who wear glasses.

	Wear glasses	Do not wear glasses	Total
Boys	8%	34%	42%
Girls	16%	42%	58%
Total	24%	76%	100%

If the school has 1750 pupils, find the number of:
(a) boys who wear glasses
(b) girls who wear glasses
(c) pupils who wear glasses
(d) boys at the school
(e) girls at the school.

8 400 students were entered for the Technology examination. The results were:

Grade	Percentage
A	9
B	14
C	41
D	32
E	4

Find the number of students who obtained:
(a) a grade C (b) a grade A or B
(c) a grade B, C or D.

9 Naomi, Wendy and Lisa enter a competition and win the first prize of £1244. They agree to share the prize so that
    Naomi has 36%
    Wendy has 29%
    Lisa has 23%
The rest of the money they give to charity.
Find:

(a) the percentage they give to charity
(b) the amount they give to charity
(c) how much Naomi receives
(d) how much Wendy and Lisa receive together.

10 Find:

(a) 10% of £240
(b) 5% of £240
(c) 2·5% of £240
(d) 17·5% of £240

The people of Ancient Rome did not use the same number symbols that we do.

When they traded in the market place they used their hands to show numbers.

Their symbols for 1, 2, 3 were straightforward

1   **I**
2   **II**
3   **III**

but their symbol for 4 looks unusual, it was

4   **IV**

To understand this you need to know that their symbol for **5** was **V**

This was because the **V**

stood for a handful of five fingers.

So our 4 was their IV because it meant **one before a handful** or **one less than five**.

1 Explain what these Roman numerals mean:
  (a) VI for 6   **(b)** VII for 7   **(c)** VIII for 8

Their symbol for our 10 was

X

because it stood for two handfuls.

2 Explain why they used:
  (a) IX for 9   **(b)** XI for 11   **(c)** XIV for 14

3 What would be the Roman way of writing:
  (a) 12   **(b)** 17   **(c)** 18   **(d)** 20   **(e)** 29?

The other symbols the Romans used were

50 L   100 C   500 D   1000 M

So **67** would be **LXVII** and
  124 would be **CXXIV**

4 Write each of these using Roman numerals:
  (a) 73   **(b)** 156   **(c)** 510   **(d)** 783   **(e)** 1995

The numbers we use today are **Arabic** numbers.
  0   1   2   3   4   5   6   7   8   9

5 Write each of these Roman numbers in Arabic numbers.
  (a) XV   **(b)** CC   **(c)** CLIV   **(d)** MDCIX
  (e) MMM

6 These sums are written in the Roman way. Find the answers, which you should also write in the Roman way.
  (a) X + IX   **(b)** D – VIII   **(c)** L × X
  (d) X × C   **(e)** M ÷ D

7 Draw a clock face and use Roman numerals to show the hours.

8 On a clock face the hours are shown using Roman numerals. The minute hand is pointing to II and the hour hand is between VII and VIII.
What time is the clock face indicating?

9 Write the following Roman numbers in order, starting with the smallest.
XI, CIX, LVIII, M, DXXXVI

The generation game

What sequence of numbers will be generated by this flow diagram?

input
1 to 5 → ×2 → +3 →

Input 1 to 5 means 'start with the number 1, work out the answer, then input 2, then 3 and so on up to 5'

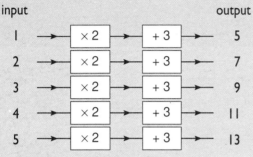

input | | | output
1 → ×2 → +3 → 5
2 → ×2 → +3 → 7
3 → ×2 → +3 → 9
4 → ×2 → +3 → 11
5 → ×2 → +3 → 13

The sequence generated is 5, 7, 9, 11, 13

1 Work out the sequence generated by each of these flow diagrams:

(a) input
2 to 5 → ×2 → −3 →

(b) input
3 to 6 → +4 → ×3 →

(c) input
5 to 2 → −1 → ×5 →

(d) input
6 to 10 → take away 4 →

(e) input
5 to 0 → take away from 4 → +2 →

(f) input
1 to 5 → divide into 12 →

2 Work out the input instructions for these flow diagrams:

(a) input
? → ×3 → +1 → 7, 10, 13

(b) input
? → −3 → ×2 → 6, 4, 2, 0

input
2 to 8
step 2   means 'start with 2 and work out the answer, then use 4, then use 6, then use 8'

This flow diagram

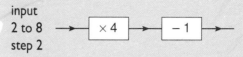

input
2 to 8 → ×4 → −1 →
step 2

will generate the sequence 7, 15, 23, 31

3 Work out the sequence generated by:

(a) input
4 to 10 → +3 → ×2 →
step 2

(b) input
1 to 10 → ×4 → −3 →
step 3

(c) input
4 to 19 → take away from 20 →
step 5

(d) input
1 to 3 → ÷2 → +0·5 →
step 0·5

4 Work out the input instructions for these flow diagrams:

(a) input
? → ×2 → +1 → 5, 9, 13
step ?

(b) input
? → −4 → ×3 → 0, 3, 6, 9
step ?

5 Work out the instructions in the box for these flow diagrams:

(a) input
1 to 4 → ? → 2, 4, 6, 8

(b) input
2 to 5 → ? → 4, 5, 6, 7

(c) input
1 to 4 → ? → 9, 8, 7, 6

1 For her maths homework Toni was asked to find out something about equivalent fractions.

In one of her maths books she found these equivalent fractions.

(a) Explain how the numerator increases.

(b) Explain how the denominator increases.

(c) What would be the next equivalent fraction in the sequence?

(d) How many times bigger is the denominator than the numerator?

2 Toni found another set of equivalent fractions.

$$\frac{3}{4} = \frac{9}{12} = \frac{27}{36} = \frac{81}{108}$$

(a) Explain how the numerator grows.

(b) Explain how the denominator grows.

(c) What is the next equivalent fraction in the sequence?

(d) How many times bigger is the denominator than the numerator?

Equivalent fractions can be made by multiplying the numerator and denominator by the same number each time.

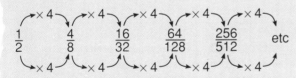

3 Write 3 more equivalent fractions for each, starting with:

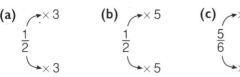

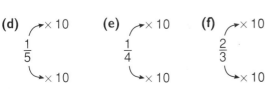

It is often necessary to write a fraction in its lowest terms. This means finding the simplest equivalent fraction.

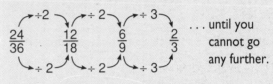

To find a fraction in its lowest terms reverse the process used at the beginning of this exercise. Divide the top and bottom number **by the same number**.

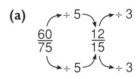

... until you cannot go any further.

$\frac{24}{36}$ in its lowest terms is $\frac{2}{3}$

4 Copy and continue until you cannot go any further.

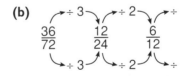

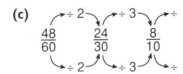

(c)
```
     ÷2      ÷3      ÷
   48      24       8
   60      30      10
     ÷2      ÷3      ÷
```

5 Write each of these fractions in its lowest terms:

(a) $\frac{18}{21}$ (b) $\frac{10}{40}$ (c) $\frac{16}{24}$ (d) $\frac{25}{40}$

6 Copy and complete.

(a) $\frac{8}{20} = \frac{?}{5}$

(b) $\frac{12}{32} = \frac{?}{8}$

(c) $\frac{15}{18} = \frac{5}{?}$

(d) $\frac{9}{27} = \frac{1}{?}$

(e) $\frac{16}{20} = \frac{?}{5}$

(f) $\frac{9}{21} = \frac{3}{?}$

(g) $\frac{10}{15} = \frac{?}{3}$

(h) $\frac{75}{100} = \frac{15}{?} = \frac{?}{4}$

Counter explosion 1

These are the rules for generating a sequence of numbers.

Rule 1 A red counter always produces a red and a yellow counter.

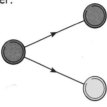

Rule 2 A yellow counter only produces a red counter.

These are the first three generations, starting with a red counter.

1st   **2nd**   **3rd**

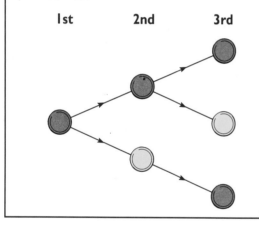

▶ **You need Worksheet 1.**

1 **(a)** Colour the first three generations as shown above.
   (b) Complete the colouring of the worksheet using the two rules given at the top of this page.
   (c) Use your completed diagram to work out the number of red counters and the number of yellow counters there will be in the fourth generation.

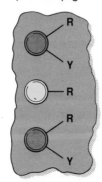

2 Copy and complete.

Generation	Number of reds	Number of yellows
1st	1	0
2nd		
3rd		
4th		
5th		
6th		
7th		

3 Extend your table up to the 10th generation, explaining the method you use.

4 Copy and complete.

Generation	Total number of counters
1st	1
2nd	
3rd	
4th	
5th	
6th	
7th	
8th	
9th	
10th	

5 Extend your table up to the 15th generation explaining the method you use.

6 Now produce a diagram of your own, using the same rules but starting with a yellow counter.

7 Copy and complete.

Generation	Number of yellows	Number of reds
1st	1	0
2nd		
3rd		
4th		
5th		
6th		
7th		

8 How many counters in total will there be in the 12th generation?

1 Grampa Jo lights this candle on his birthday cake.
   This table shows the height, *h,* in cm of the candle
   after time, *t,* in minutes.

   (a) How high was the candle before it was lit?
   (b) For how long did the candle burn?

Time (*t*)	0	1	2	3	4	5	6
Height (*h*)	12	10	8	6	4	2	0

   (c) Make a copy of this diagram on graph paper.

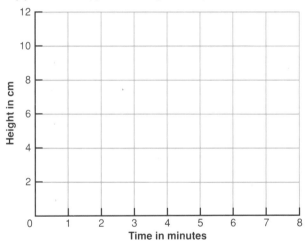

   (d) Plot the points from the table and join them up
   with a straight line.
   (e) Use your graph to find the height of the candle
   2·5 minutes after it was lit.
   (f) How long had the candle been burning before it
   reached a height of 2·5 cm?

2 A second candle 8 cm high is lit at the same time as
   the one on Grampa Jo's cake and lasts for 8 minutes.
   (a) Show this information on the same graph as
   question 1.
   (b) How long after they are lit are both candles the
   same height?
   (c) What is the burn rate, in cm per min, of both
   candles?

3 For her daughter's birthday
   cake Sangeeta buys a special
   candle.
   This table shows the height,
   h, in cm of this candle after
   time, *t,* in minutes.

Time (*t*)	0	1	2	3	5	8	11
Height (*h*)	11	5	3	2	1	0·75	0

   (a) How tall was Sangeeta's candle before it was lit?
   (b) For how long did it burn?
   (c) On graph paper draw a pair of axes. The vertical
   axis, *h,* is numbered up to 12.
   The horizontal axis, *t* minutes, is also numbered
   up to 12.
   (d) Plot the points from your table and join them
   with a smooth curved line.
   (e) What was the height of the candle after it had
   been lit for 1·5 minutes?
   (f) How long did it take to reach a height of 2·5 cm?
   (g) When the candle reached half its original height,
   how long had it left to burn?

4 This graph shows the height, *h* cm, of a third type of
   candle after time, *t* minutes.

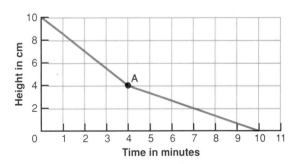

   (a) Write the coordinates of point A.
   (b) What was the burn rate in cm per min after it
   was lit, until it reached point A?
   (c) What was the burn rate after it had reached
   point A?

Sasha gave Freeman this problem to solve.

I think of a number, multiply it by 4, then add 5 to this result to give an answer of 33. What number did I originally think of?

I need to draw a flow diagram for this.

I think of a number

$n \longrightarrow \boxed{\times 4} \longrightarrow \boxed{+ 5} \longrightarrow 33$

To work out the answer to Freeman's problem

- draw a second flow diagram adding instructions opposite to those in the first diagram. This is called a loop diagram

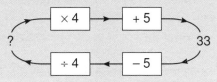

- work through the opposite instructions and complete the loop to find the missing number

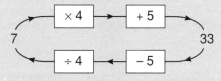

- check that you have found the correct answer by working through the original part of the loop

$7 \times 4 = 28$

$28 + 5 = 33$

You need a calculator.

1 Use loop diagrams to solve each of these problems.

(a) I think of a number, multiply it by 4 and then add 12. The answer is 52.

(b) 7 is added to a certain number and then the result multiplied by 6. This gives an answer of 72.

2 Use loop diagrams to solve each of these puzzles. Remember to check your answers.

(a) I think of a number, add 2·5 and then multiply the result by 4. This gives an answer of 24.

(b) 5 is subtracted from a certain number and the result divided by 2, to give an answer of 4.

(c) A number is doubled and 6·5 taken away from the result. This leaves an answer of 4·5.

(d) I think of a number, multiply it by 5, add 8, to get an answer of 20.

(e) A number is squared and 5·75 added to give a result of 48.

(f) A number has 12 taken away from it and the result multiplied by 8, to give an answer of 44.

Freeman sets Sasha a different problem to solve.

I think of a number, add 5, then multiply by 2. From this result I subtract 7 to give me an answer of 16. Find the number!

This time Sasha needs three instruction boxes.

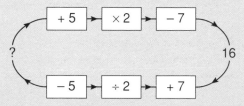

Work through the loop to get an answer of 6·5.

3 Now solve these puzzles.

(a) I think of a number and add 6, multiply the result by 5, and take away 4. This leaves an answer of 46.

(b) A number is doubled and 5 added. This result is divided by 2 to leave 7.

(c) A number is divided by 3, and 4 is subtracted. This result is multiplied by 11 to give a final answer of 55.

(d) I think of a number, add 4, then square the result. I subtract 40 from this to leave an answer of 32·25.

1 (a) What type of numbers are in the second row of this table?

Number	1	2	3	4	5	6	7	8	9	10
?	1	4	9	16	25	36	49	64	81	100

(b) Make a copy of the table and extend it as far as the 12th square number.

2 Show that these squares can be placed together to make one larger square.

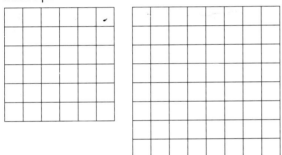

3 Jamie has made these two large squares from several small squares.

(a) Which two square numbers does each large square represent?

(b) Show that the two squares can be 'added' to make a third square number using all the squares.

Nelson has been asked if a 5 by 5 square and a 12 by 12 square can be 'added' to make a larger square and if so, what size it will be.

$$5 \times 5 = 5^2 = 25$$
$$12 \times 12 = 12^2 = \underline{144}$$
add the answers $\underline{169}$

square root $\sqrt{169}$ to give 13

The answer to Nelson's problem is 'yes' and the new square will be 13 by 13.

4 Which of these can be added to make a larger square? For those that can be added, write the area of the new square.

(a) $4^2 + 6^2$ **(b)** $10^2 + 24^2$ **(c)** $7^2 + 24^2$

(d) $9^2 + 12^2$ **(e)** $15^2 + 36^2$ **(f)** $18^2 + 60^2$

(g) $25^2 + 40^2$ **(h)** $21^2 + 72^2$ **(i)** $1 \cdot 5^2 + 2 \cdot 5^2$

(j) $0 \cdot 6^2 + 0 \cdot 8^2$

A conference was arranged between Eastland and Westland.

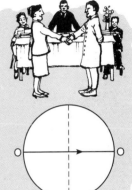

This diagram represents the two officials shaking hands.

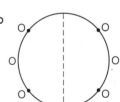

5 (a) Complete this diagram to show the handshakes if both countries sent two officials.

(b) How many handshakes will take place?

6 (a) Complete this diagram to show the number of handshakes if both countries sent three officials.

(b) How many handshakes will take place?

7 (a) Draw a diagram to show the number of handshakes if both countries sent 4 officials.

(b) How many handshakes will take place?

(c) What type of numbers are the 'number of handshakes'?

8 How many handshakes will take place if each country sent:

(a) 6 officials   **(b)** 10 officials

(c) 25 officials   **(d)** 60 officials?

9 At one conference there were 2025 handshakes. How many officials did each country send?

Get primed

The **factors** of a number are all the numbers that will divide into it without a remainder.

1 Write the factors of:
   (a) 20   (b) 23   (c) 44   (d) 75   (e) 90

A number that has only 2 factors is a prime number.

2 Write the factors of:
   (a) 5   (b) 9   (c) 15   (d) 17   (e) 19

These are the factors of 12   {1, 2, 3, 4, 6, 12}

The **prime numbers** which are factors of 12 are 2 and 3
They are the **prime factors** of 12

The prime factors of a number are the prime numbers that will divide into it without a remainder.

3 Which of the numbers in question **2** are prime numbers?

4 Write:
   (a) the factors of 20
   (b) the prime factors of 20
   (c) the prime factors of 23.

Tree diagrams can be used to find the prime factors of a number.

Starting number

split into 2 numbers

keep splitting
until all the
numbers are prime

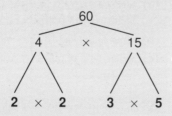

$2 \times 2 \times 3 \times 5 = 60$

and the prime factors are 2, 3 and 5
(All the prime numbers are listed only once.)

You need a calculator.

5 (a) Copy and complete this tree diagram.

   (b) Write the prime factors of 252.

6 (a) Copy and complete this tree diagram.

   (b) Write the prime factors of 770.
   (c) Show, by drawing a second tree diagram, that the same prime factors are obtained if the number 770 is split into 70×11 instead of 10×77

7 By drawing a tree diagram, or using any other method, find the prime factors of:
   (a) 525   (b) 1386   (c) 2600

8 These are the first 7 square numbers
   1, 4, 9, 16, 25, 36, 49, 64
   (a) Only one of these numbers has more than one prime factor. Without drawing any tree diagrams, work out which number it is.
   (b) Now work out how many **factors** each of these square numbers has.
   (c) Copy and complete these statements.

A number which has only ☐ factors is a prime number.

A number which has an ☐ number of factors is a square number.

9 Use your answers to question **8** to help you answer this ancient problem.
   'Is it possible to find a number that is both square and prime?'
   Give reasons for your answer.

The photograph shows a country scene.

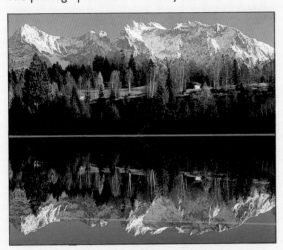

The countryside is **reflected** in the lake.
The **mirror line** or **line of symmetry** has been drawn in bold.
The reflection is known as **the image.**

1 Copy each of these shapes.
On each one draw the line of symmetry.

(a) **(b)** **(c)**

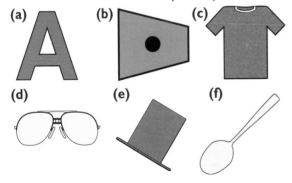

(d) **(e)** **(f)**

2 Copy each drawing.
In each case, draw the reflection of the shape in the bold line.

(a) **(b)** **(c)**

(d) **(e)** **(f)**

You need squared or graph paper.

3 (a) Plot the points
A(1, 1) B(1, 4) C(4, 4)
and draw the triangle ABC.
The triangle ABC is reflected in the vertical axis (known as the y axis) to give the triangle PQR.

(b) Draw the triangle and give the coordinates of P, Q and R.

4 (a) Copy this diagram onto squared or graph paper.

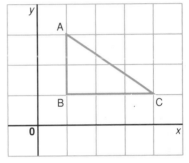

(b) Reflect the triangle ABC in the bold line.
(c) Write the coordinates of the vertices of the reflected triangle.

5 (a) Draw a triangle with vertices P, Q and R where P is ($^-$2, 5) Q is (2, 1) and R is (2, $^-$6). This triangle is reflected in the horizontal axis (known as the x-axis) to give the triangle LMN.

(b) Find the coordinates of L, M and N.

6 The diagram shows the two lines $y = x$ and $y = {}^-x$

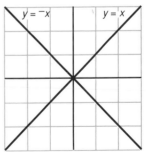

Find the coordinates of the image of the point:
(a) (3, 1) after a reflection in the line $y = x$
(b) (2, 5) after a reflection in the line $y = x$
(c) ($^-$3, 4) after a reflection in the line $y = {}^-x$
(d) (5, $^-$3) after a reflection in the line $y = {}^-x$
(e) (4, 7) after a reflection in the line $y = {}^-x$
(f) ($^-$3, $^-$2) after a reflection in the line $y = {}^-x$

Louise's logo

Louise is designing a logo for her T shirt.

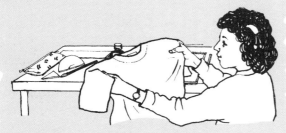

• She starts her design with a ▽ shape

• she rotates the ▽ shape through a right-angle (90°) about the corner to make

• she rotates it again to make

• she rotates it one more time to complete her logo.

The final logo has **4 rotational symmetries** or **rotational symmetry of order 4** through angles of 90°, 180°, 270° and 360° (or 0°)

1 ▶ Do Worksheet 2.

2 Write the number of rotational symmetries for each of these shapes.

(a)   **(b)**   **(c)**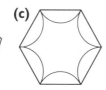

3 Find the order of rotational symmetry of:
  (a) a square
  (b) a rectangle which is not a square
  (c) a regular pentagon
  (d) a regular hexagon
  (e) a regular octagon
  (f) a regular shape with *n* sides.

4 Explain why any 2D shape must always have at least one rotational symmetry.

5 Sketch a shape with rotational symmetry of order:
  (a) 3   **(b)** 5   **(c)** 4   **(d)** 8

In each case give the angle of rotation.

6 What is the order of rotational symmetry of:
  (a) a parallelogram
  (b) a rhombus
  (c) a regular 20 sided shape
  (d) an equilateral triangle
  (e) a circle?

7 Write the capital letters of the alphabet. State the order of rotational symmetry of each letter.

8 Write the number of rotational symmetries for each of these flags.

(a)   **(b)**   **(c)**

(d)   **(e)**   **(f)**

9 Make an arrangement of 5 dots that has rotational symmetry of order 4.

10 On this 3 by 3 grid

one square can be shaded in.
Find the possible orders of rotational symmetry for the shaded shape. Explain your answer.

Gulzar and her family are going to tour Ireland for their holiday. Gulzar will act as the navigator. She knows the **eight main compass points**.

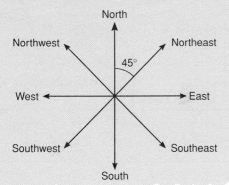

Gulzar has a map of Ireland which she will use to help navigate their journey.

1 Write the value of the clockwise angle between the directions:
   (a) north and east
   (b) south and north
   (c) west and east
   (d) east and north
   (e) northeast and west
   (f) southwest and southeast
   (g) west and southwest
   (h) southeast and north
   (i) northwest and east
   (j) northwest and south
   (k) west and southeast
   (l) southeast and west.

2 Write the anti-clockwise angles between each of the directions given in question 1.

The direction north-northeast is given by the line which is halfway between north and northeast. It is usually written as NNE.

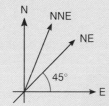

3 Draw a diagram of the eight main compass points and on it mark and label each of these directions.
   (a) NNW   (b) SSW   (c) WSW   (d) ENE

4 Write the names of the town or towns approximately:
   (a) due west of Dublin
   (b) due north of Wexford
   (c) east of Athlone
   (d) west of Belfast
   (e) north of Cork
   (f) east of Tralee
   (g) southwest of Belfast
   (h) southeast of Galway
   (i) north-northwest of Athlone
   (j) south-southwest of Galway.

5 Help Gulzar identify the only town which is:
   (a) almost due north of Tralee and due west of Dublin
   (b) to the south of Belfast and southwest of Athlone
   (c) to the south of Donegal, almost due west of Dublin and north of Waterford.

6 Write estimates of the angles between the lines joining:
   (a) Belfast to Athlone and Athlone to Dublin
   (b) Galway to Dublin and Tralee to Dublin
   (c) Wexford to Galway and Galway to Belfast
   (d) Wexford to Athlone and Waterford to Athlone
   (e) Dublin to Belfast and Belfast to Donegal
   (f) Athlone to Dublin and Athlone to Galway
   (g) Donegal to Dublin and Dublin to Tralee
   (h) Cork to Donegal and Belfast to Galway.

Coordinates 1

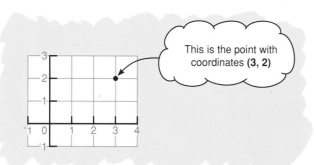

This is the point with coordinates (**3, 2**)

You need squared paper.

1 **(a)** Plot the points ABCD
   A (2, 1)   B (5, 1)   C (5, 3)   D (2, 3)
   (b) Join the points to make the rectangle ABCD.
   (c) Calculate the area of ABCD.

2 **(a)** Write the coordinates of the three vertices,
   P, Q and R of the triangle.

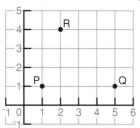

   (b) Find the area of the triangle.

3 Liam is playing a board game.
   He places a counter at the point (0, 0)
   Then he rolls a red die and a blue die.
   If the red die shows 3 and the blue die shows 5 it
   means that Liam must move his counter 3 places to
   the right and five places up.
   (a) Draw a 12 × 12 grid and show the places Liam
       should move his counter to when:
       • the red die shows 4 and the blue die shows 1
       • the red die shows 5 and the blue die shows 6
   (b) Liam has the following sequence of throws
       red = 2, 4, 5   blue = 1, 6, 2
       Find the coordinates of the finishing point for his
       counter.

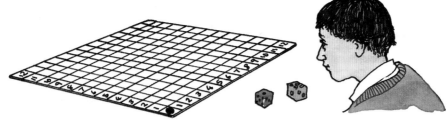

4 The triangle ABC is reflected in the mirror line to
   give the image A'B'C'.

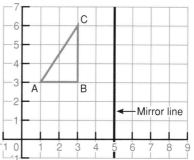

Write the coordinates of A', B' and C'

5 The point X is the centre of a square.
   The point A is one of the corners of that square.

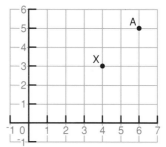

   (a) Find the coordinates of the other three corners
       of the square.
   (b) Calculate the area of the square.

6 The point X is the centre of a square and A is one of
   its vertices.

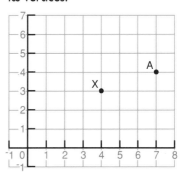

Find the coordinates of the other three vertices.

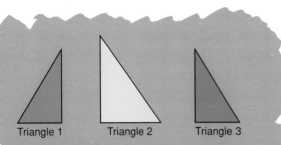

Triangle 1   Triangle 2   Triangle 3

Triangles 1 and 3 are the same as each other in every respect. They are just facing in different directions.
The words used to describe this fact are

triangles 1 and 3 are congruent
or
triangle 3 is congruent to triangle 1.

1 ▶ **Do Worksheet 3**.

2 Which triangles are congruent to triangle A?

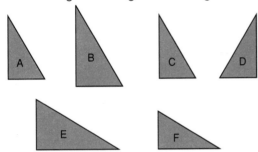

3 Each of these triangles has been labelled with a letter. Put the triangles into three congruent pairs.

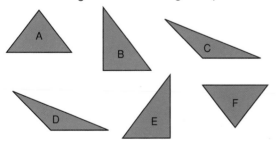

4 Which shapes are congruent to rectangle A?

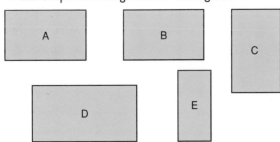

This triangle is reflected in the mirror line.

triangle   image

This creates another triangle called the **image** of the first triangle.

5 Will the two triangles above be congruent? Explain your answer.

You need squared paper.

6 (a) Plot each of the three triangles
ABC where A = (1, 1) B = (3, 1) and C = (3, 4)
PQR where P = (4, 2) Q = (5, 3) and R = (5, 1)
LMN where L = (6, 5) M = (9, 5) and N = (6, 7)
(b) Which two of these triangles form a congruent pair?
(c) Draw and label a fourth triangle which is congruent to the odd one out of the first three triangles.

You need tracing paper.

7 (a) Use your tracing paper to make an exact copy of the shape below.

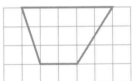

(b) Make an exact copy of the shape in your book.
(c) Draw two other shapes which are both congruent to the original shape.

8

(a) Copy this drawing of a nine-pin board.
(b) Draw lines that divide the board into two congruent halves.
(c) Repeat this as many times as possible.

9 Are any two capital letters in the alphabet congruent? Explain your answer.

The **perimeter** of a 2D shape is the distance around the shape. The **area** of a 2D shape is the amount of space inside it.

The **perimeter** of the shape above is
3 + 2 + 3 + 2 = 10 centimetres
because that is the total distance around the shape.

The **area** of the shape above is
6 square centimetres
because the shape has **6** small squares inside it and each square is a one centimetre square.

1 Work out the perimeter and area of each of these shapes:

(a)   (b)   (c)

(d)   (e)   (f)

 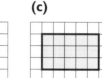

The **perimeter** of any shape is always found by adding the lengths of its sides.

The **area** of different shapes can be found in many different ways. You may know some of them. Some are examined later in this book.

When a shape is drawn on squared paper you can find its area by counting the squares or part squares inside it. In some cases you might have to make estimates.

The **area of a rectangle** can always be found by multiplying the length of the rectangle by the width of the rectangle.

To calculate the perimeter and area of the rectangle

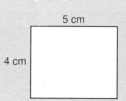

Perimeter = 4 + 5 + 4 + 5 = **18 cm**
Area = 4 × 5 = **20 cm^2**

2 Find the perimeter and area of each shape.

(a)   (b)   (c)

(d)   (e)   (f)

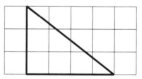 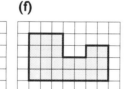

3 This triangle has been drawn on squared paper.

For the triangle:
(a) measure the lengths of the sides
(b) calculate the perimeter
(c) find, by any method, its area.

4 The perimeter of a rectangle is 20 cm. The length of the rectangle is 6 cm. Calculate:
(a) the width
(b) the area of the rectangle.

You need a ruler.

5 (a) Measure the length and width of the piece of paper you are writing on.
(b) Record your results.
(c) Calculate:
  • the perimeter
  • the area of that piece of paper.

This is the **net** of an open-topped box. The net is a flat shape you can fold to make the box.

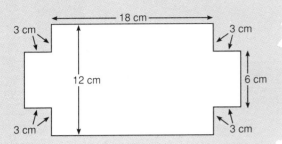

You need thin card, sticky tape, scissors and a supply of 1 cm cubes.

1 On your card draw an accurate copy, to the exact size, of the net of the box above. Fold the net and make the box.
Lay a row of cubes on the base of the box so that the whole of the base is fully covered with cubes.

(a) Count or work out the number of cubes you need to cover the base of the box.

(b) How many cubes will you need to fill the box completely?

(c) What are the length and width of the base of the box in centimetres?

(d) What is the height of the box?

(e) Work out (length of the base × width of the base × height of the box).

(f) Confirm that your answer to (e) is the same as the number of cubes needed to fill the box.

2 Repeat what you have done in question 1 for this net.

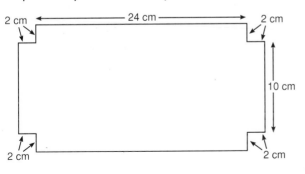

3 This is the net of a triangular-based box. Make the box out of thin card. Estimate the number of one centimetre cubes needed to fill the box completely.

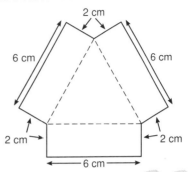

The amount of space inside a box is the **volume** of the box. When the sides of the box are measured in centimetres, the volume is measured in cubic centimetres. This measurement of volume is equal to the number of one centimetre cubes needed to fill the box completely.

4 Work out, in any way you can, the volume of the box that would be made from each of these nets.

(a)

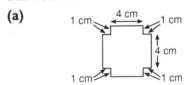

(b)

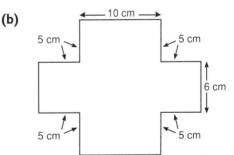

(c)

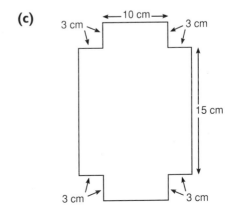

Statistical diagrams

Bar charts

This **bar chart** shows how students travel to a school.

Bar charts are used to display information that can be counted.

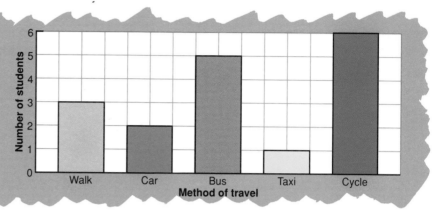

1 The number of different trees in a small wood are given by the data in the table.

Type of tree	Birch	Oak	Willow	Sycamore	Poplar
No of trees	3	10	8	4	7

Draw a bar chart to display this information.

Pictograms

This **pictogram** shows how students travel to a school.

Pictograms are used to display information about items that can be counted and represented using **symbolic** pictures.

Walk	🚶 🚶 🚶				
Car	🚶 🚶				
Bus	🚶 🚶 🚶 🚶 🚶				
Taxi	🚶				
Cycle	🚶 🚶 🚶 🚶 🚶 🚶				

2 Draw a pictogram of the different types of tree shown in the table in question 1, using these symbols.

Birch	🌳	Oak	🌳	Willow	🌳	Sycamore	🌿	Poplar	🌲

Pie charts

This **pie chart** shows how Joanne spent her time during one 24-hour period.

Pie charts are **usually** used to display information that can be counted. Because she spent $\frac{1}{4}$ of the day at school, the angle for 'At school' is $\frac{1}{4}$ of $360° = 90°$

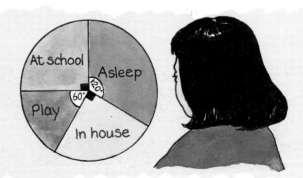

3 Draw a pie chart to illustrate the information shown in the table below about the weather on the 30 days in November one year.

Type of weather	Sunny	Rain	Cloudy	Fog	Snow	Sleet
No of days	4	10	8	5	2	1

Bar line graphs

This **bar line graph** shows the shoe sizes of 21 people.

Bar line graphs are used in a similar way to bar charts, show frequency distributions of items that can be counted.

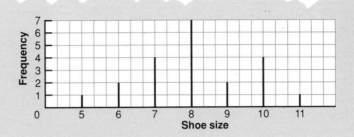

4 The table below gives information about the number of people living in a house.

Number of people	0	1	2	3	4	5	6
Frequency	2	5	8	6	4	2	1

Draw a bar line graph for this frequency table.

Line graphs

This **line graph** shows the monthly rainfall in Miami.

Line graphs are used to show trends over a period of time.

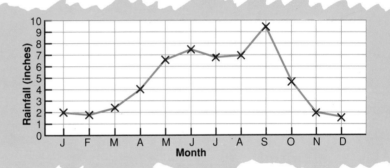

5 **(a)** Draw a line graph to show the monthly temperature in °C for Miami shown in the table below.
Start your vertical axis at 15°C.

Temperature (°C)	19	20	21	23	25	27	28	28	27	25	22	20
Month	J	F	M	A	M	J	J	A	S	O	N	D

(b) Work out the mean monthly temperature for Miami.

Statistical diagrams

Histograms

50 students entered a competition.
The **grouped frequency** table shows the scores they gained.

Score	21–30	31–40	41–50	51–60	61–70	71–80	81–90	91–100
Frequency	1	2	7	15	13	8	3	1

Histogram to show the scores of the 50 students.

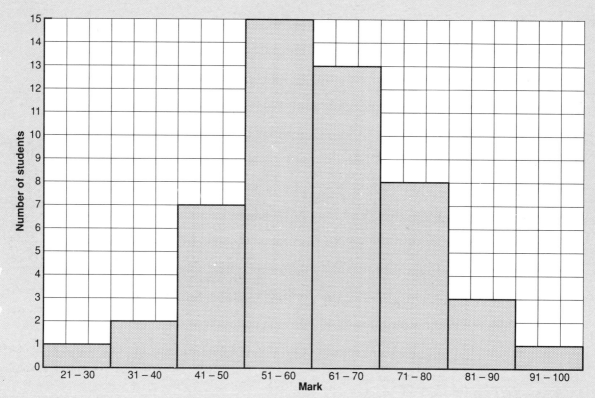

In a histogram there are no gaps between the bars.

---

6 The marks obtained by 60 students in a French test are shown in the grouped frequency table.

Mark	1–4	5–8	9–12	13–16	17–20
Frequency	3	8	13	27	9

Draw a histogram to illustrate this data.
(Remember to label the axes and give your diagram a title.)

7 The heights of 50 adults are given in the table below.

Height, (h) cm	Frequency
$140 < h \leqslant 150$	1
$150 < h \leqslant 160$	6
$160 < h \leqslant 170$	11
$170 < h \leqslant 180$	18
$180 < h \leqslant 190$	10
$190 < h \leqslant 200$	3
$200 < h \leqslant 210$	1

Draw a histogram to illustrate this data.
(Remember to label the axes and give the diagram a title.)

The McAlister family are planning their holiday.

They know that they want to go to
Italy or **Spain**
but are undecided about which country to go to.

They are also undecided about the means of travelling. They do know that they will be travelling by **Air, Coach** or **Rail**

The family know that there are several possibilities and find it confusing.

James McAlister has learnt about **decision trees** at school.

He draws a decision tree that will help his family to see all the possibilities.

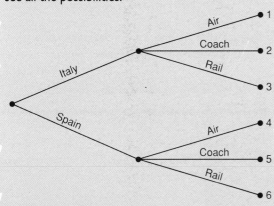

James explains that the decision tree shows
6 different possibilities.

He sets these out in a table

Italy by Air	Spain by Air
Italy by Coach	Spain by Coach
Italy by Rail	Spain by Rail

1 Jack McAlister was very impressed with decision trees. He has decided that it is time to buy a new car. He knows that the make of car they want will be
Ford   Datsun   or   **Peugeot**

The colour they want will be either
Red   White   or   **Blue**

   (a) Draw a decision tree to show Jack all the possible choices he can make.

   (b) How many different possibilities are there?

2 Helen McAlister says they should buy either a **Hatchback** or an **Estate** car.

   (a) Show how this will alter the decision tree.

   (b) How many different possibilities are there now?

   (c) List all these possibilities.

3 The McAlister family buy their new car before they book their holiday. Elspeth, James' sister, suggests that now they have a new car they could use it to take them on holiday.

   (a) Construct a new decision tree for the McAlister family which shows all the possibilities for going to either Italy or Spain and travelling by air, coach, rail or car.

   (b) List all of these possibilities.

   (c) How many possibilities are there?

4 Helen McAlister suddenly realises that because of the school holidays they can only go away in either July or August.

   (a) Create a new decision tree which includes the two months in which they can take their holiday.

   (b) How many different possibilities are there now?

5 The McAlister family discuss the accommodation they might use.
The four possibilities are
Hotel   Tent   Caravan   Apartment

   (a) Draw another decision tree which shows all the possibilities related to **country, means of travel, month of the holiday** and **type of accommodation**.

   (b) How many different possibilities do they now have to consider?

When a coin is tossed in the air it has an equal chance of landing **heads** or **tails**.
The coin has I chance out of 2 of landing heads.
We say that
the probability of the coin landing heads is $\frac{1}{2}$

You can show probability on a probability scale or line.

This line goes from 0 to 1 and is marked in quarters.

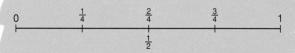

A probability of **I** means that something is **certain**.
A probability of **0** means that something is **impossible**.

I Here are some things that can happen.
Write your estimate for the probability of each one happening.
Mark each event on a probability line using fractions:
(a) that the next baby to be born will be female
(b) that a die will land with three showing
(c) that a die will land with an odd number showing
(d) that a playing card will be a heart
(e) that it will be warm in August
(f) that a pig can fly
(g) that a letter of the alphabet will be a vowel
(h) that when one of ten balls numbered from 0 to 9 is selected it will be ball number 4

2 A bag contains 20 coloured balls.
Ten of the balls are red, four are blue, three are white, two are green and one is black.
A ball is selected from the bag without anyone looking, that is, it is selected **at random**.
What is the probability that the ball selected will be:
(a) red   (b) blue   (c) white
(d) green   (e) black?

Give your answers as fractions and record them on a probability line.

Probability can also be recorded as a decimal, on a scale from 0 to 1.

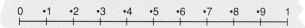

3 Repeat questions **I** and **2**, but this time mark all the probabilities on the line as decimals.

4 A computer can choose any whole number from I to 100 at random.
What is the probability that the computer will choose:
(a) the number 25
(b) the number 50
(c) a number ending in 0
(d) a number ending in 5
(e) a number in the twenties?

Mark your answers on a probability line using decimals.

Probability can also be recorded as a percentage, but the scale goes from 0 to 100%

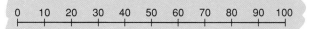

5 Repeat questions **I** and **2** again but this time mark the probabilities on the line as percentages.

6 Write three things which have the following probabilities of happening:
(a) 50%   (b) 25%   (c) 10%   (d) 100%

Martyn and Sara have made two spinners.

Martyn's spinner has two equal portions, red and blue. Sara's has three equal portions, black, white and green.

They each spin their spinner and record the **outcome**.

The outcomes from Martyn's spinner are that it could land **red** or it could land **blue**.

There are just **two** different outcomes.

1 List the outcomes for Sara's spinner.
How many different outcomes are there?

Martyn spins his spinner twice. Two of the outcomes of doing this are

First spin	Second spin
red	**blue**
blue	**blue**

---

2 List all of the different possible outcomes when Martyn spins his spinner twice.
How many such outcomes are there?

Martyn spins his spinner three times. One of the outcomes could now be

First spin	Second spin	Third spin
red	**red**	**blue**

---

3 List all the possible outcomes when Martyn spins his spinner three times.
How many such outcomes are there?

4 List all the possible outcomes when Sara spins her spinner:
 (a) twice
 (b) three times.
How many different outcomes are there in each case?

5 Work out the number of different outcomes when Martyn spins his spinner:
 (a) 4 times   **(b)** 5 times.

6 (a) Copy and complete this table for Martyn spinning his spinner.

No of spins	No of different outcomes
1	2
2	
3	
4	
5	
6	

 (b) Use the table to work out the number of different outcomes when Martyn spins his spinner 10 times.

7 Work out the number of different outcomes when Sara spins her spinner:
 (a) 4 times   **(b)** 5 times.
How many different outcomes are there in each case?

8 (a) Copy and complete this table for Sara's spinner.

No of spins	No of different outcomes
1	3
2	
3	
4	
5	
6	

 (b) Use your table to find the number of different outcomes when Sara spins her spinner 10 times.

Martyn and Sara spin their spinners once each but at the same time. Two of the outcomes of this **joint event** are

Martyn's spinner	Sara's spinner
red	**green**
blue	**black**

---

9 (a) List all the different possible outcomes when Martyn spins his spinner twice and Sara spins her spinner twice. They both spin their spinners at the same time.
 (b) How many such different outcomes are there?

Chances

Sinead and her family love playing all sort of games of chance, such as cards, snakes and ladders, and computer games.

Many things in life can be a bit chancy. When things can happen by chance we use **probability**.

The word **probability** is a way of **measuring our belief that something will happen**.

> Probability is always written as a
> **fraction, decimal or percentage**.

When we toss a coin it can land either **Heads** or **Tails**. We have no reason to believe that the coin is any more or any less likely to land heads rather than tails.

So there are **two outcomes** both of which have the same **chance** or both of which are **equally likely**.

Because landing heads has **1 chance out of 2 possibilities**, and because **these two possibilities are equally likely**, we write this as
    probability of landing Heads = $\frac{1}{2}$
or more simply
    p(H) = $\frac{1}{2}$
In the same way
    p(T) = $\frac{1}{2}$

We could also write these probabilities as decimals, so
    p(H) = 0·5   and   **p(T) = 0·5**

We could also write these probabilities as percentages, so
    p(H) = 50%   and   **p(T) = 50%**

1 Write as fractions, decimals and percentages the probabilities that:
  (a) the next baby to be born will be male
  (b) a die will land with a 3 on its top face
  (c) a card chosen at random from a pack will be a club.

Sometimes we have to use statistical evidence to help us work out a probability.

If we asked 100 people to name their favourite colour and 40 people answered red, our evidence would suggest that

the probability of someone's favourite colour being red is

$\frac{40}{100}$ or   **0·4**   or   **40%**

These would be our **best estimates** of that probability.

Of course, the more people we ask about their favourite colour, the more accurate the estimate we can make of probability.

2 Two hundred students were asked to name their favourite school lunch. The replies were:

Favourite lunch	No of students
Beefburgers	80
Salad	50
Sandwiches	40
Fish fingers	30

Writing your answers as fractions, decimals and percentages in each case, find the probability that the favourite lunch is:
  (a) beefburgers   **(b)** salad
  (c) sandwiches   **(d)** fish fingers.

3 A second group of 200 students was asked the same question. Their replies were:

Favourite lunch	No of students
Beefburgers	60
Salad	40
Sandwiches	60
Fish fingers	30
Curry	10

Find the estimates of the probabilities based on only this evidence. Again give your answers as fractions, decimals and percentages in each case.

4 Combine the two sets of results into a table for the 400 students who were asked the question about their favourite school lunch.

Use the combined results to find new estimates for the probabilities.

Which set of results, the first, the second or the combined ones, are likely to produce the best estimates?

5 Carry out a very quick favourite food survey amongst the people in your class. Give the estimates of probabilities suggested by the results.

You need a die, coin and a pack of playing cards. Work in pairs or small groups for the next three questions.

6 (a) A coin is tossed. What is the probability that it will land Heads?

(b) Toss a coin 20 times. Record whether it lands Heads or Tails.

(c) Write the fraction

$$\frac{\text{number of Heads}}{\text{number of times the coin was tossed}}$$

(d) Is the fraction in **(c)** close to your answer for **(a)**? Explain.

7 (a) What is the probability that a die will land with:
  • the number 3 on its top face
  • the number 5 on its top face.

(b) Roll the die 60 times. Record the number shown on the top face each time.

(c) Write each of the fractions

  • $$\frac{\text{the number of times 3 was on the top face}}{\text{the number of times the die was rolled}}$$

  • $$\frac{\text{the number of times 5 was on the top face}}{\text{the number of times the die was rolled}}$$

(d) Are the two fractions in **(c)** nearly equal to each other? Explain.

(e) Are the two fractions in **(c)** nearly equal to the answers you gave in **(b)**? Explain.

8 (a) A pack of playing cards is shuffled well and the top card selected without anyone looking at it. What is the probability of the top card being a heart?

(b) Follow these instructions 40 times:
  • Shuffle the pack of cards.
  • Take off the top card and record whether it is a club, diamond, heart or spade.
  • Replace the card in the pack.

(c) Write the fraction

$$\frac{\text{number of times a heart was recorded}}{\text{number of shuffles etc made}}$$

(d) Comment on whether or not the fraction in **(c)** is close to your answer in **(a)**.

9 When you cross over the road you will either get across or be run over.
Comment on the statement:
'the probability of being run over is $\frac{1}{2}$'

10 A hockey team can either win, lose or draw a match. Why is it impossible to say that the probability of Scotland winning their next match is $\frac{1}{3}$

11 Give a very brief explanation of how you could give an estimate of the probability of a hockey team winning a match. Why might this estimate still be very unreliable?

12 The major television channels are

BBC1   BBC2   ITV   Channel 4

It is known that every Tuesday at 7.30 pm approximately 30 million people watch television. It is also known that every Tuesday at 7.30 pm approximately 20 million people watch Eastenders on BBC1.
A company conducts a survey into people's television viewing habits. They conduct their survey for Tuesdays at 7.30 pm.

(a) Is it likely that a result of their survey will be the probability of viewer watching BBC1 at 7.30 on a Tuesday is $\frac{1}{2}$?

(b) If your answer to **(a)** is YES then explain why. If your answer to **(a)** is NO, give a better estimate for the probability.

Imran has a sequence of numbers.

2, 5, 10, 17, 26, 37, 50,

He wants to find the next number in this sequence.

Donna shows Imran what to do.

You take the first number away from the second. This gives 3.

Then you take the second number away from the third to get 5.

We call this getting the differences and it helps you find the next number in the sequence.

Donna then sets up a **difference table** for Imran.

Sequence	2		5		10		17		26		37
Differences		3		5		7		9		11	

She tells Imran that the next number in the difference row has to be 13. So the next number in the sequence will be **37 + 13 = 50**

1 What will be the next two numbers after 50 in Imran's sequence?

2 What will be the:
   (a) 10th number in Imran's sequence
   (b) 15th number in Imran's sequence?

3 Find the next two numbers in each of these sequences:
   (a) 2, 5, 8, 11, 14, 17, ...
   (b) 3, 8 13, 18, 23, 28, ...
   (c) 4, 8, 12, 16, 20, 24, ...
   (d) 4, 9, 16, 25, 36, 49, ...
   (e) 3, 8, 15, 24, 35, 48, ...
   (f) 2, 4, 7, 11, 16, 22, ...
   (g) 6, 9, 14, 21, 30, 41, ...
   (h) 1, 4, 8, 13, 19, 26, ...
   (i) 42, 38, 34, 30, 26, 22, ...
   (j) 2, 5, 12, 25, 51, 103, ...

To find the next number in a sequence it sometimes helps to take the **differences of the differences**.
These are called the **second differences**.
Donna and Imran look to see how this works with the sequences

0, 1, 5, 15, 34, 65

They construct the difference table.

Sequence	0		1		5		15		34		65
1st Differences		1		4		10		19		31	
2nd Differences			3		6		9		12		

This helps them to see that
the next number in the 2nd differences row is 15
so the next number in the 1st differences row must be
31 + 15 = 46

and the next number in the sequence must be
65 + 46 = 111

4 Find the next two numbers in each of these sequences. In each case show your working and give your reason.
   (a) 0, 2, 5, 9, 14, 20, ...
   (b) 1, 8, 27, 64, 125, 216, ...
   (c) 0, 1, 6, 18, 40, 75, ...
   (d) 1, 2, 9, 25, 53, 96, ...
   (e) 1, 5, 21, 55, 113, 201, ...

5 Find the next two numbers in each of these sequences. Using differences may or may not help. Take care. Give all of your working and reasons.
   (a) 2, 4, 8, 16, 32, 64, ...
   (b) 1, 2, 3, 5, 8, 13, ...
   (c) 1, 3, 5, 6, 9, 14, 20, ...
   (d) 1, 3, 7, 15, 31, 63, ...
   (e) 3, 5, 7, 9, 9, 13, 11, 17, ...

A drinks machine will accept only 5p, 10p and 20p coins.

For a drink costing 20p, Ivan can put into the machine any of these coins.

These coins can be used in any order.

For a drink costing 20p, Ivan has **3 different** choices of coin selection.

1 How many different choices does Ivan have for a drink that costs:

   (a) 30p   **(b)** 40p?

2 Drinks in a certain machine can cost anything from 15p to £1.
   Investigate the different choices of coin selection for drinks within this range of prices.

3 A second drinks machine will accept 5p, 10p, 20p and 50p coins. Drinks in this machine also cost anything from 15p to £1.
   Investigate the different choices of coin selection for drinks from this second machine.

Liam is playing a board game, Gridlock.

He places a counter at the point (0, 0)

Then he rolls a black die and a white die.

If the black die shows 3 and white die shows 2, it means that Liam should move his counter 3 places to the right and two places upwards.

Liam can roll the dice any number of times.

1 Show the position of Liam's counter when:
  (a) the black die shows 4 and the white die shows 6
  (b) both dice show 3
  (c) the black die shows 2 and the white die shows 5.

2 Show the final positions of the counter when:
  (a) the black die shows 3 followed by 2 followed by 2, and the white die shows 4 followed by 2 followed by 1
  (b) black shows 4, 4, 2, 1 and white shows 3, 4, 1, 1.

3 What is the furthest point the counter can be away from its starting point after three rolls of each die?

4 After 3 rolls of each die Liam has moved the counter to (6, 12). **Investigate** the sequences of scores for which this is possible.

5 Extend the investigation in question **4** to other points and other numbers of rolls of the dice.

Helen is making a pattern of hexagons out of matchsticks.

The hexagons must all be in a row.
Helen has made a row with 5 hexagons.
She has used **26** matchsticks.

1 Find the number of matchsticks Helen will need to make a row of:
(a) 6 hexagons
(b) 10 hexagons
(c) any two numbers of hexagons of your own choice.

2 **Investigate** the number of matchsticks she will need to make various numbers of hexagons.

3 What is the **maximum** number of hexagons that Helen can make if she has:
(a) 16 matchsticks
(b) 126 matchsticks
(c) 1000 matchsticks?

4 **Examine briefly** the situation if Helen lifts the restriction that all of the hexagons must be in a row.

Show all of your working for your answers.
Give full explanations.
Make and test any general results.

Missed by a mile

> 1 kg is approximately 2·2 lb
> 8 km is approximately 5 miles
> 1 litre is approximately 1·75 pints
> 1 gallon is equal to 8 pints

1 Every week Sandra, salesperson for County Kitchens, has to fill in a travel log showing all the distances she has travelled. For each mile she has travelled she is paid 50p.

(a) Copy and complete her travel log.

County Kitchens			
Day	Distance travelled		Amount claimed
	miles	km	
Monday	25		£12·50
Tuesday	35		£17·50
Wednesday		48	
Thursday		64	
Friday	60		
Saturday		100	
Sunday			£37·50

(b) How many miles did she travel during the week?

(c) The following week Sandra claimed £112·50. How may kilometres did she travel?

2 Jane Walker used to buy 4 pints of milk every day from her milkman.

(a) How many pints a week did she buy?

She now buys her milk from the supermarket which only sells 1 litre cartons, but she needs to buy the same amount of milk.

(b) How many cartons should she buy each week?

3 The weights of 10 students in class 4B in lbs were

(a) What is the weight of the heaviest student in kg?
(b) What is the total weight, in kg, of all ten students?

4 If the petrol tank of a small car holds 8 gallons of petrol find how much it:

(a) holds in pints
(b) holds in litres
(c) costs to buy a full tank of petrol.

£2·54 gallon

5 At 56 mph a car can travel 50 miles on one gallon of petrol. At 70 mph the same car can only travel 44 miles.
Calculate:

(a) how far, in km, the car can travel on one gallon of petrol at a speed of 70 mph
(b) the difference, in km, it can travel on one gallon of petrol, between travelling at 56 mph and 70 mph
(c) how many litres of petrol it takes to travel 50 miles at 56 mph
(d) the car's consumption in km/litre when travelling at 70 mph.

6 Kashmir is completing a science project. Part of the project is to find out the weight of various liquids. Find the weight, in kg, of 1 litre of water.

water 1 gallon weighs 10lb

7 This packet of digestive biscuits contains 32 biscuits.

(a) Find the weight of
  • the packet in lb
  • one biscuit in grams
  • 40 biscuits in lb
  • 50 biscuits in kg.

Digestive Biscuits 500g

(b) Find how many biscuits there are in $\frac{3}{4}$ lb.

1 These were the temperatures at midday and midnight on Christmas Eve, in five cities in the British Isles.

	Midday	*Midnight*
Leeds	4°C	⁻4°C
Belfast	2°C	⁻6°C
Glasgow	⁻1°C	⁻8°C
Edinburgh	0°C	⁻9°C
Southampton	8°C	1°C

(a) Which city had the lowest midnight temperature?

(b) Which city had the highest midday temperature?

(c) What was the difference between the midday and midnight temperatures in Edinburgh?

(d) What was the difference between the midday temperature in Leeds and the midnight temperature in Glasgow?

(e) On Boxing Day the recorded temperatures in Belfast were 4°C lower than those on Christmas Day. What were both the midday and midnight temperatures in Belfast on Boxing Day?

2 At the end of the day Julie looks at the bank statement of 7 customers. The statement reads:

(a) How much money do the following have between them:
- Keith and Dagjit
- Sandra and Carol
- Peter, Sally and Roger?

(b) What is the difference between the amounts of money the following have:
- Roger and Peter
- Sandra and Sally?

(c) What is the balance if all 7 accounts are added together?

3 The accounts of 6 more of Julie's customers are:

Southland Bank		
end of day 26·9·92 statement		
NAME	BALANCE	
Jagjit	£5 Credit	(⁺5)
Errol	£3 Debit	(⁻3)
Graham	£4 Credit	(⁺4)
Roy	£8 Credit	(⁺8)
David	£10 Debit	(⁻10)
Lucy	£7 Debit	(⁻7)

Use this information to help you answer these questions:

(a) ⁺5 + ⁺4   **(b)** ⁺5 + ⁻3
(c) ⁻3 + ⁻10   **(d)** ⁻7 + ⁺8
(e) ⁺8 + ⁺4 + ⁻7   **(f)** ⁺5 + ⁺4 + ⁻10
(g) ⁺8 − ⁺4   **(h)** ⁻10 − ⁻7
(i) ⁺5 − ⁻7   **(j)** ⁻3 − ⁺8
(k) ⁺5 + ⁻3 − ⁺4   **(l)** ⁻7 − ⁻10 + ⁺4
(m) ⁻3 − ⁺4 − ⁺5   **(n)** ⁺8 − ⁻7 − ⁻3

4 This is Sean's bank statement. Next week he needs £150 deposit for his holiday. How much money does he need to pay the deposit and clear his bank account?

Southland Bank	
name Sean Bates acc no 2077191191 sort	
DATE	BALANCE
12/1/94	£52 Credit
15/1/94	£43 Credit
23/2/94	£15 Credit
1/3/94	£24 Debit
16/4/94	£63 Debit

5 Write the next two terms of these sequences of numbers.

(a) 2, 5, 7, 11, . . .
(b) 9, 7, 5, 3, . . .
(c) 8, 4, 0, ⁻4, . . .
(d) ⁻7, ⁻5, ⁻3, ⁻1, . . .
(e) ⁻25, ⁻20, ⁻15, ⁻10, . . .
(f) 4, ⁻2, 3, ⁻3, 2, ⁻4, . . .
(g) 6, ⁻6, 4, ⁻4, 2, ⁻2, . . .

6 What total do you get if you add together all the numbers, starting with Peter, and going:
(a) clockwise
(b) anti-clockwise?

All for one . . .

During the first part of his journey Ben travels 120 km in 3 hours. How far does he travel in 2·5 hours?

If in 3 hours he travels 120 km
in 1 hour he will travel 120 ÷ 3 = 40 km
and therefore
in 2·5 hours he will travel 40 × 2·5 = 100 km

1 During the second part of the journey Ben travels 125 km in 5 hours. Find how far he:
   (a) travelled in 1 hour
   (b) would travel in 6 hours
   (c) travelled in 3 hours 30 minutes.

2 A packet of ginger biscuits contains 16 biscuits and weighs 200 grams. Find the weight of:
   (a) one biscuit
   (b) 10 biscuits
   (c) 25 biscuits.

3 Find the cost to the nearest penny of:
   (a) one tile
   (b) 15 tiles.

style tiles
18 tiles
£6·90

4 Jean works as a computer programmer and earns £356 for a 40 hour week.
Find:
   (a) her hourly rate
   (b) the amount she would earn if she worked a normal week plus 8 hours overtime paid at time and a half.

5 A supermarket sells Wizard washing up liquid.
Find:
   (a) the cost of one millilitre
   (b) the number of millilitres per penny.

£2·20
Wizard
500ml

6 During an international crisis the exchange rate between the British pound and the American dollar almost reached an all-time low.

The **DAILY RECORD**
BRITAIN IN CRISIS!
POUND ALMOST AT ALL-TIME LOW OF £1 = $2

If the newspaper had been correct:
   (a) how many dollars would you have been given for
      • £12   • £20
   (b) how much money, in pounds, would you have been given for $1
   (c) how many pounds would you have been given for $5?

7 A bottle of white correction fluid contains 20 ml of fluid and costs 72p. Find:
   (a) the cost of 1 ml
   (b) the amount of fluid per penny
   (c) the cost of a 100 ml bottle of correction fluid assuming that the cost per ml is charged.

8 The larger bottle of KoKe contains 3 litres of liquid and costs £1·44. The standard bottle contains 2 litres and costs 92p. Work out, giving your reason, which of these bottles is the 'best buy'.

KoKe £1·44 3 litres
KoKe 92p 2 litres

9 A book 3 cm thick contains 480 pages. Find:
   (a) how thick, in millimetres, one page of the book will be
   (b) how thick the first 100 pages of the book will be
   (c) the number of pages in a book 2·1 cm thick
   (d) how thick 5 books will be, if each book has 256 pages.

Ken Rice, the local builder, is building a new house. He needs to dig a trench by the side of the house in which to lay drains. The trench is 30 metres long.

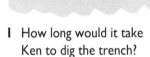

Ken can dig a length of 3 metres in one day.

1 How long would it take Ken to dig the trench?

2 Ken's son, Anthony, works with him. They decide to dig the trench together. How long would it take them both working together, and at the same rate, to dig the trench?

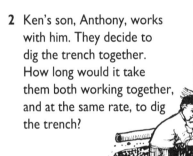

3 Ken decides that even working with his son it would still take too long to dig the trench and so he employs three more builders to help them dig it.

How long will it take Ken, Anthony and the other three builders to dig the trench?

4 A second, smaller trench is also needed for the drains. This trench is 24 metres long and can be dug by one man at a rate of 4 metres per day. Find how long it would take to dig it if:

(a) Ken works alone

(b) Ken and Anthony work together

(c) Ken, Anthony and one other builder work together

(d) a gang of 15 people all dig together.

Six builders start work on Monday morning to build a wall. It takes them three days to complete it. How long would it take two builders to build a similar wall?

If it takes six builders three days then it must take two builders longer to build a similar wall.

The way to solve this type of problem is to work out how long it would take for **one** builder to build the wall.

It would take one builder 6 × 3 = 18 days

Therefore 2 builders must take 18 ÷ 2 = 9 days

5 Ken employs five electricians. Working together, these electricians can wire up a new house in two days. How long should it take:

(a) one electrician working on his own to wire one house

(b) four electricians to wire the same house?

6 Carol has to complete the plumbing. She works out that if she spends two hours a day it will take her six days to complete it. How long would it take her if she spent three hours a day on it?

Percentages 2

These are Shaminder's results for her half-term tests. In which subject did she do best?

It is difficult to compare the results because they have all been marked out of a different total. It is easier to compare the results by changing the fractions into decimal fractions.

PARKLANE HIGH SCHOOL
Half-term school report
Shaminda Gupta
ENGLISH 43/50
SCIENCE 54/60
MATHS 35/40

English $\frac{43}{50} = 0.86$

Science $\frac{54}{60} = 0.9$

Maths $\frac{35}{40} = 0.875$

Putting these results in size order
0·9 (Science), 0·875 (Maths), 0·86 (English)
Shaminder obtained her best mark in Science.

1 These are Mark's results for the same exams.

PARKLANE HIGH SCHOOL
Half-term school report
Mark Watts
ENGLISH 28/50
SCIENCE 33/60
MATHS 23/40

(a) Change each result into a decimal fraction.

(b) In which subject did Mark do best?

Instead of changing each fraction into a decimal fraction it is more usual to change them into percentages.

0·86   means $\frac{86}{100} = 86\%$

0·9   means $\frac{90}{100} = 90\%$

0·875 means $\frac{875}{1000} = \frac{87.5}{100} = 87.5\%$

2 Write each of these decimal fractions as a percentage.

(a) 0·24   (b) 0·78   (c) 0·55   (d) 0·6
(e) 0·35   (f) 0·06   (g) 0·02   (h) 1·25

To change a decimal fraction into a percentage multiply the decimal by 100

⟶ 0·75 ⟶ ×100 ⟶ 75%

3 Change these fractions into percentages by first changing them into decimal fractions and then multiplying by 100.

(a) $\frac{1}{2}$ (b) $\frac{2}{5}$ (c) $\frac{13}{20}$

(d) $\frac{32}{40}$ (e) $\frac{39}{50}$ (f) $\frac{27}{40}$

(g) $\frac{42}{60}$ (h) $\frac{42}{90}$ (i) $\frac{30}{45}$

4 These are Sangeeta's results for her half-term exams.

PARKLANE HIGH SCHOOL
Half-term school report
Sangeeta Puri
DESIGN   30/36
TECH   42/50
MATHS   36/40
ENGLISH   43/50
SCIENCE   52/60

(a) Change all the results into decimal fractions.

(b) Change the decimal fractions into percentages.

(c) Re-write Sangeeta's school report with the subjects in size order, with the best result first.

At Park Lane High, 12 students out of a class of 32 were absent with flu. What percentage were absent?

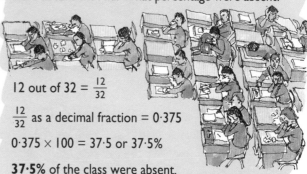

12 out of 32 = $\frac{12}{32}$

$\frac{12}{32}$ as a decimal fraction = 0·375

0·375 × 100 = 37·5 or 37·5%

37·5% of the class were absent.

5 Park Lane High has 800 students. 240 cycled to school. What percentage cycled to school?

6 Out of 80 students, 12 were chosen for the chess team. What percentage of the students were chosen?

7 During an experiment with a spinner, George obtained these results. Copy and complete his table.

Colour	Number of times	Percentage of total number of spins
red	6	
green	11	
blue	14	
white	9	

The same method can still be used when the amounts are not whole numbers.

What percentage of £5·80 is £2·40?

2·4 out of 5·8 = $\frac{2·4}{5·8}$ = 0·41 to 2 dp.

0·41 ⟶ ×100 ⟶ 41%

8 Express the first quantity as a percentage of the second.

(a) 4·5 km, 7·2 km
(b) 3·4 kg, 12·8 kg
(c) 6·6 cm, 1·2 m
(d) 0·5 g, 1·8 g
(e) 73·5 ml, 108 ml
(f) £2·45, 1243 p

9 Jimmy the jeweller was making an alloy by mixing 1·4 kg of silver with 7·8 kg of copper. What percentage of the alloy was:

(a) silver
(b) copper?

10 James went on a diet. Find the amount of weight:

(a) he lost
(b) he lost as a percentage of his starting weight.

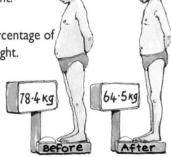

78·4 kg — Before
64·5 kg — After

11 This table shows the number of members of the Samurai Sports Club who wear glasses.

	Wear glasses	Do not wear glasses	Total
Males	42	112	154
Females	54	97	151
Total	96	209	305

What percentage of:

(a) males wear glasses
(b) females wear glasses
(c) the membership wear glasses
(d) the membership is female?

12 (a) Measure the length of each side of this triangle.
(b) Calculate the length of each side as a percentage of the perimeter.

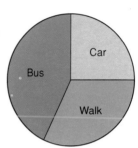

13 This pie chart shows the results of a survey of how people travel to work.

(a) Measure the angle of each sector.
(b) Calculate the percentage of people who travel by bus.

Car
Bus
Walk

14 Kwic-repair and Speedy-fit both sell car tyres for £36·50. Kwic-repair increase their price by 6% whereas Speedy-fit increase the price of their tyres by £2·20.

(a) Calculate the percentage increase in the price of Speedy-fit tyres.
(b) Which garage should you shop at to get the best buy?

15 This advertisement appeared in the *Henley Herald*.

DEN'S DISCOUNT STORE
THE BEST VALUE IN TOWN
GUARANTEED LOWEST PRICES
UP TO 40% DISCOUNT
BUY NOW!
Save £££'s

	Normal Price	OUR PRICE	You SAVE
Alarm system	£199·99	£130·00	£69·99
Control panel	£68·75	£44·50	£24·25
Dimmer switches	£18·85	£11·31	£7·54
13 Amp sockets	£5·68	£3·90	£1·70

(a) What is the percentage discount on the alarm systems?
(b) Which item carries the 40% discount?

16 Three sisters own a machine tool company. Brenda owns $\frac{2}{5}$ of the shares, Carol $\frac{1}{3}$ and Dianne $\frac{4}{15}$. What percentage of the shares do Carol and Dianne own between them?

Getting closer

James has to calculate the length of the side of a square so that the area is correct to 3 decimal places using a trial and improvement method.

He starts by measuring the length of the side on the drawing. He finds it is 4·7 cm. He then starts his calculations like this:

Since it is a square, the area is the length squared or length × length so

4·7 × 4·7 = 22·09   too small
4·8 × 4·8 = 23·04   too big

> the answer lies between 4·7 and 4·8

Try 4·74   4·74 × 4·74 = 22·468 to 3 dp   too small
Try 4·75   4·75 × 4·75 = 22·562 to 3 dp   too big

> the answer lies between 4·74 and 4·75

Try 4·743   4·743 × 4·743 = 22·496 to 3 dp
Try 4·744   4·744 × 4·744 = 22·506 to 3 dp

> the answer lies between 4·743 and 4·744

Try 4·7435   4·7435 × 4·7435 = 22·501 to 3 dp
Try 4·7434   4·7434 × 4·7434 = 22·500 to 3 dp

The length of the side of a square to give the area correct to 3 decimal places is 4·7434 cm.

Area = 33·5 cm²

1 **(a)** Measure the length of one side of the square as accurately as you can.
   (b) Multiply your answer by itself and see how close you are to the correct area.
   (c) Using the trial and improvement method find the length of one side so that the area is correct to 3 decimal places.

2 For her maths homework Paula has to find the angle at the centre of a circle when it is divided into 7 equal sectors. She knows the answer can be found by dividing 360 by 7 but the 'divide' button on her calculator is broken. Using only the multiplication button and the trial and improvement method, Paula found the answer correct to 4 significant figures. Now solve Paula's problem showing all your workings.

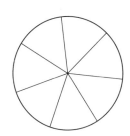

3 Using the trial and improvement method, find the length of this rectangle so that the area is correct to 4 dp. Show all your working.

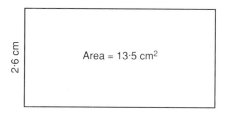

2·6 cm

Area = 13·5 cm²

4 Using the trial and improvement method, find the cube root of 10 correct to 3 dp. Show all your working.

This is the end view of a garage.

Let b equal the length of the base

let h equal the height to the top of the roof

let s equal the height to the bottom of the roof

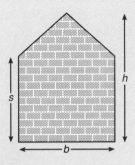

The area of the garage wall can be found using the formula

$$\text{Area} = \frac{b(s + h)}{2}$$

You need a calculator.

1 Find the area when:

(a) $b = 3$ m, $s = 3$ m and $h = 4$ m

(b) $b = 3{\cdot}5$ m, $s = 3$ m and $h = 3{\cdot}6$ m

(c) $b = 2{\cdot}4$ m, $s = 3{\cdot}2$ m and $h = 3{\cdot}5$ m

(d) $b = 3{\cdot}2$ m, $s = 2{\cdot}75$ m and $h = 3{\cdot}25$ m

2 The approximate area of an equilateral triangle can be found using the formula

$$\text{Area} = \frac{0{\cdot}86s^2}{2}$$

where s is the length of one side

Find the area when:

(a) $s = 4$ (b) $s = 6{\cdot}5$ (c) $s = 22{\cdot}4$

3 The total surface area of this chocolate box can be found using the formula

$$\text{Area} = 2(lw + lh + hw)$$

where l is the length

w is the width

h is the height

Find the total surface area when:

(a) $l = 10$ cm, $w = 6$ cm and $h = 2$ cm

(b) $l = 12$ cm, $w = 8$ cm and $h = 2{\cdot}5$ cm

(c) $l = 8$ cm, $w = 6{\cdot}4$ cm and $h = 2{\cdot}5$ cm

(d) $l = 10{\cdot}4$ cm, $w = 5{\cdot}8$ cm and $h = 3{\cdot}4$ cm

4 The approximate volume of a cone can be found using the formula

$$V = 0{\cdot}78d^2h$$

where d is the base diameter

h is the vertical height

Find the volume of a cone when:

(a) $d = 6$ cm and $h = 10$ cm

(b) $d = 3{\cdot}2$ cm and $h = 6{\cdot}4$ cm

(c) $d = 8{\cdot}5$ cm and $h = 12$ cm

(d) $d = 8{\cdot}2$ cm and $h = 12{\cdot}2$ cm

5 Joe Striker is given a trial with Shimpling United. He plays four games. His mean score rate can be found using the formula

$$S = \frac{a + b + c + d}{4}$$

where

a is the number of goals scored in the 1st game

b is the number of goals scored in the 2nd game

c is the number of goals scored in the 3rd game

d is the number of goals scored in the 4th game

Find the mean score rate when:

(a) $a = 3$, $b = 0$, $c = 2$ and $d = 1$

(b) $a = 2$, $b = 3$, $c = 1$ and $d = 2$

(c) $a = 4$, $b = 1$, $c = 3$ and $d = 5$

6 The height of the back of a pick up truck above ground level depends upon the weight in the back. The height can be found using the formula

$$h = 120 - \frac{w^2}{16}$$

where w is the weight in kg.

Find the height above the ground to the nearest cm, when:

(a) $w = 15$ kg   (b) $w = 22{\cdot}5$ kg

(c) $w = 32$ kg   (d) $w = 40$ kg

7 What is the maximum weight that can be put into the back of the truck before it touches the ground?

Formulate an answer

The perimeter of a rectangle can be found by adding the length and width together and multiplying the result by 2

This statement can be translated into maths shorthand like this:

Let P = the perimeter $P = \boxed{\ ?\ }$

Add the length and width together $(l + w)$

Multiply the result by 2 $2(l + w)$

The perimeter, P, is $P = 2(l + w)$

1 Use the formula above to find the perimeter of a rectangle of length 12 cm and width 8 cm.

2 The mean (average) of 4 numbers can be found by adding the four numbers together and dividing the result by 4
  (a) Translate this sentence into maths shorthand by letting m be the mean and the 4 numbers be n, o, p and q
  (b) Calculate the mean when $n = 5, o = 7, p = 9$ and $q = 3$.

3 The area of a trapezium can be found by calculating the mean of the two parallel sides and multiplying this result by the height.

  (a) Translate the previous sentence into maths shorthand.
  (b) Calculate the area of this trapezium.

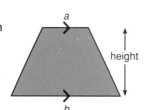

6 cm
5 cm
11 cm

4 Joan earns £n per hour and works h hours a week.
  (a) Write a formula for working out the amount of money Joan earns in a week.
  (b) Calculate the amount when $n = £6$ and $h = 35$ hours.

5 Dynamic Drains make two charges when they are called out to clear a blocked drain. The first charge is a fixed call-out charge. The second charge is an hourly rate for the time it takes to complete the work.

  (a) Work out a formula for finding the total price charged for a call-out and having a blocked drain cleared.
    Let P = the total price charged in £s
    Let C = the call-out charge in £s
    Let R = the hourly rate in £s
    Let T = the time taken to complete the work in hours.
  (b) Calculate the total price a customer has to pay when the call-out charge is £25 and it takes the plumber 5 hours to clear a drain at the rate of £7 per hour.

6 Mark is designing a new kitchen layout. He is going to put up 4 wall cabinets along one wall of his kitchen. He wants to keep the layout symmetrical and decides the gaps at each end must be equal.

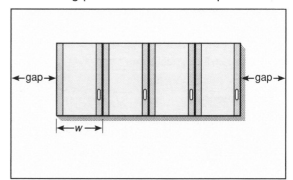

  (a) Find a formula for working out the gap when Mark knows the length of the kitchen and the width of a wall unit.
  (b) Find the length of the gap when the kitchen is 3·5 metres long and the width of one wall unit is 500 mm.

Angela has a simple problem.

> I think of a number and take away 5 to get an answer of 3.

This problem can be shown on a flow diagram.

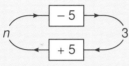

- 5

n 3

+ 5

Completing the loop, the answer is 8   Check $8 - 5 = 3$

She has a second problem.

> I think of a number and take it **away from** 5 to get an answer of 3.

This is the flow diagram,

Take away from 5

?   3

?

but what is the opposite of 'take away from 5'?

To help find the answer first solve the problem
$5 - ? = 3$ The answer is 2
$5 - 2 = 3$

Put this answer into the loop diagram.

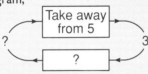

Take away from 5

2   3

?

1 **(a)** Try to work out the missing instructions in the flow diagram. The title of this topic will give you a clue.
   (b) When you think you have worked out the answer, test it on this flow diagram.

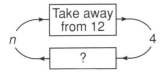

Take away from 12

n 4

?

If it doesn't work, think again.

2 Solve these problems by drawing loop diagrams.

   (a) I think of a number, take it away from 11 to get an answer of 8

   (b) A number is taken away from 10 and then multiplied by 4 to give an answer of 14

   (c) The number I am thinking of is divided by three and then taken away from 8 to leave an answer of 10

   (d) Multiply this number by 4, add 5 and take the result away from 30 to get an answer of ⁻9

   (e) I think of a number, multiply it by 6, take this result from 25 and then divide by 2. The answer I get is ⁻7.

3 Solve this problem by drawing loop diagrams, but be careful, there are two answers. Try to find both.

> I think of a number, add 4, then square the result. I subtract this result from 40 to leave ⁻9.

Loop diagrams can be used to solve equations written in symbols.

The equation can be represented by this flow diagram.

$4n + 7 = 18$

→ ×4 → +7 →

4 Solve the equation above by copying and completing the loop diagram.

5 Solve these equations by first drawing a flow diagram to represent them and then completing the loop.
   (a) $5n + 7 = 25$ **(b)** $6 + 2n = 17$
   (c) $4n - 8 = 3$ **(d)** $3n - 11 = 4$
   (e) $25 - 2n = 16$ **(f)** $4 - 5n = ⁻6$
   (g) $3n + 16 = ⁻2$ **(h)** $2n - 0.5 = 23$

6 Solve these equations:
   (a) $\frac{2n + 6}{4} = 12$ **(b)** $\frac{5n - 11}{2} = 16$
   (c) $3(2n + 1) = 6$ **(d)** $4(5 - 3n) = 12$
   (e) $8(5n - 6) = ⁻12$ **(f)** $\frac{4(6 - 2n)}{3} = 15$

Running out of time

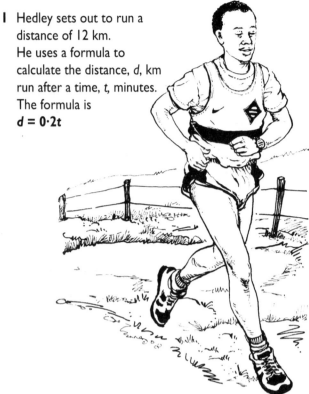

1 Hedley sets out to run a distance of 12 km.
He uses a formula to calculate the distance, *d*, km run after a time, *t*, minutes.
The formula is
d = 0·2t

(a) Use Hedley's formula to copy and complete this table.

Time (mins)	0	10	20	30	40	50	60
Distance (km)	0						

(b) On graph paper make a copy of this diagram.

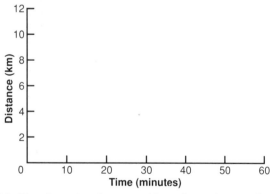

(c) Plot the points in your table and join them with a straight line.
(d) How long did it take Hedley to complete his run?
(e) How long did it take him to run 5 km?
(f) How far has Hedley run after 15 minutes?
(g) How fast was he running in km per min?

2 David, Hedley's brother, sets out 10 minutes after Hedley to run the same route.

David uses this formula,
d = 0·24(t − 10)
where *d* is the distance
t is the time after Hedley starts
(a) Copy and complete the table.

Time (mins)	10	20	30	40	50
Distance (km)					

(b) Plot these points on the same graph as question 1.
(c) Who finished the run first, Hedley or David?

3 This rectangle has a fixed length of 8 cm but its width can be changed.

A formula for working out the perimeter is

P = 2(8 + w)

where *w* is the width.

(a) Copy and complete.

Width (cm)	1	2	3	4	5	6	7	8
Perimeter (cm)								

(b) On graph paper draw two axes, plot the points and join them with a straight line.

(c) Find the perimeter of a rectangle with a width of 4·5 cm.
(d) If a second rectangle has a perimeter of 27 cm, what is its width?
(e) What is the area of a rectangle whose width is 7·5 cm?

Here is a second set of rules for generating a sequence.

Rule 1 A black counter always produces a black and a white counter.

Rule 2 A white counter always produces a white and a grey counter.

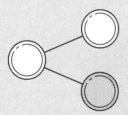

Rule 3 A grey counter always produces a white counter.

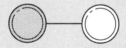

These are the first three generations of the sequence starting with a black counter.

1st   **2nd**   **3rd**

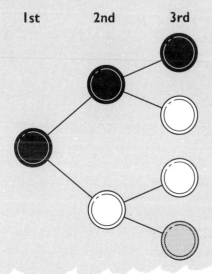

1 ▶ You need Worksheet 4.

  (a) Colour the first three generations as shown in the panel.

  (b) Complete the colouring of the worksheet using the rules given in the panel.

2 Use your completed diagram to work out the number of black, white and grey counters in the next generation.

3 Copy and complete.

Generation	Number of blacks	Number of whites	Number of greys
1st	1	0	0
2nd	1	1	0
3rd	1	2	1
4th			
5th			
6th			

4 Extend your table up to the 10th generation, explaining the method you use.

5 Copy and complete.

Generation	Total number of counters
1st	1
2nd	2
3rd	4
4th	
5th	
6th	
7th	
8th	
9th	
10th	

6 Extend your table up to the 15th generation, explaining the method you use.

7 How many counters of each colour will the 15th generation have?

Stick at it

Brian is making a pattern with some matchsticks.

This is his first pattern.

1 How many matchsticks does it take to make this pattern?

2 Brian decides to extend his pattern to

(a) How many extra matchsticks does he need?
(b) Copy Brian's design and add the next two squares.

3 Copy and complete.

Number of squares	1	2	3	4	5	6
Number of matchsticks	5					

4 How many matchsticks will Brian need to make a design with:
(a) 10 squares
(b) 20 squares?

5 Find the connection between the number of squares and the number of matchsticks.

6 Gabi is also making a design with matchsticks.
Her design is

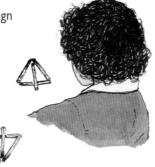

She extends her design to

How many extra matchsticks does Gabi need to extend her design?

7 Copy and complete.

Number of triangles	1	2	3	4	5	6
Number of matchsticks	4					

8 How many matchsticks are needed to make a design with:
(a) 10 triangles   (b) 20 triangles?

9 Write the connection between the number of triangles and the number of matchsticks.

10 Brian and Gabi make a combined design. Their basic design is

They extend their design to

Copy and complete.

Number of units in the design	1	2	3	4	5	6
Number of matchsticks	6	11				

11 How many matchsticks will they need to make a pattern with:
(a) 8 basic design units
(b) 15 basic design units?

12 Write the connection between the number of basic design units and the number of matchsticks.

You need a calculator.

1 What type of numbers are in the second row of this table?

Number	1	2	3	4	5	6	7
?	1	8	27	64	125	216	343

2 Make a copy of the table and extend it as far as the 10th cube number.

You need isometric squared paper.

3 On isometric squared paper draw a diagram to show how Jason can place these small cubes together to make one large cube.

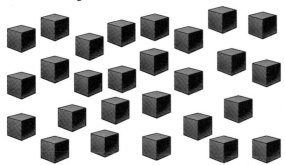

4 Jason has made these two cubes from a number of small cubes.

(a) Which two cube numbers does each diagram represent?

(b) Explain why it is not possible to make one large cube from these two smaller ones.

(c) How many extra cubes do you need to make a larger cube?

On some calculators you can find the cube root of a number like this:

Enter **1728** Press **inv** **xʸ** **3** to give **12.**

5 Which of these numbers of cubes can be made into one large cube, using all the cubes? For those cubes that can be put together into a large cube, write the length of one side of the cube.

(a) 4096   (b) 5673   (c) 15 625

(d) 32 768   (e) 45 600   (f) 68 921

(g) 75 321   (h) 97 336   (i) 100 000

$7 \times 7 \times 7 = 343$
and $3 + 4 + 3 = 10$
and $1 + 0 = 1$

When a number is split and the separate digits added, the final answer is called the **digital root**. The digital root of $7^3 = 1$

6 (a) Copy and complete.

Number	Number cubed	Digital root
1	1	1
2		
3		
4		
5		
6		
7	343	1
8		
9		
10		

(b) Write what you notice about the digital roots of cube numbers.

7 (a) Without the use of a calculator, explain why this cannot be a cube number
345621

(b) Explain why this could be a cube number
453 285

(c) Is 453 285 a cube number?

(d) Explain what the answers to parts (b) and (c) tell you.

Symmetric solids

Just as a two-dimensional shape can have a line of symmetry, so a three-dimensional shape can have a plane of symmetry.

These are some of the **planes of symmetry** of a cube.

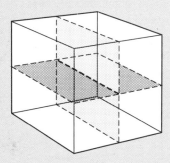

If we turn the cube through 90° about the line, then its eight corners will occupy the same eight points in space, although each corner will itself move. This line is called **an axis of symmetry**.

1 Which of these objects have at least two planes of symmetry:

   (a) a cuboid   **(b)** a sphere   **(c)** a rugby ball
   (d) a cup   **(e)** a hand   **(f)** a spoon?

2 Give three real life objects which have no planes of symmetry.

3 This is a square-based pyramid.

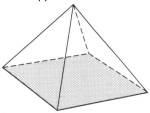

   (a) How many planes of symmetry does it have?
   (b) How many axes of symmetry does it have?

4 This is a cylinder.

   (a) How many planes of symmetry does it have?
   (b) How many axes of symmetry does it have?

5 This is a prism.
   The base of the prism is an equilateral triangle.

   (a) How many planes of symmetry does it have?
   (b) How many axes of symmetry does it have?

6 Draw a sketch of a 3D shape which has five planes of symmetry and only one axis of symmetry.

7 This is the net of a tetrahedron.

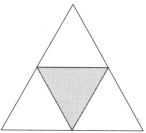

   Each face of the tetrahedron is an equilateral triangle. The actual tetrahedron looks like this.

   (a) How many planes of symmetry does it have?
   (b) How many lines of symmetry does it have?

You need a box of solid shapes.

8 Take some solid shapes.
   Try to identify the planes and axes of symmetry for each shape.
   Record your findings with diagrams.

9 Name four real life objects.
   Try to identify the planes and axes of symmetry for each object.
   Record your findings, with diagrams.

10 How many planes of symmetry and axes of symmetry does a sphere have?
   Explain your answers.

Nicky and Asif have volunteered to carry some books from the school office to a group of classrooms.

They can only carry enough books for two classrooms at a time. Each time they deliver the books to two rooms they must return to the office for some more. After delivering the last books they must return to the office.

They have a map of the school which shows the distance from the office to the classrooms and the distances between the classrooms.

This is their map. All the distances are in metres.

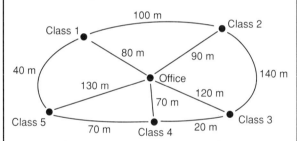

To save time and energy they want to work out the shortest possible route.

1 Work out the total distance Nicky and Asif will travel if they go to the classrooms in the order
1, 2, 3, 4, 5

2 Choose two possible orders they might choose for visiting the classrooms. Work out the total distance they will travel in each case.

3 Try to help them work out the shortest possible route.

4 Their friend, Sean, suggests that they could get a trolley and take all the books in one go. Then they can start at the office, visit all five classrooms and return with the trolley to the office.
Work out some different routes they might take and try to find the shortest route.

5 The postman, Pete, has to start at the sorting office, collect the post from six village post offices and return to the sorting office.
The distances between the sorting office and the village post offices are shown on the map below, as are the distances between the villages. All the distances are in km.

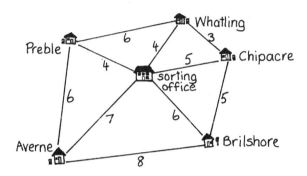

(a) Work out the total distance Pete travels if he takes the route

sorting office → Preble → Whatling
→ Chipacre → Brilshore → Averne
→ sorting office

(b) **Investigate** various routes Pete might take, and try to decide which route is the shortest.

■ **Investigation**

6 The map shows the distances in kilometres from London to some other large cities.

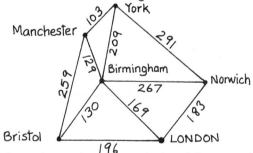

A courier service is contracted to deliver parcels to each of the cities.
The courier service collects the parcels in London and then makes one round trip to all the cities before returning to London.
Investigate a range of journeys the courier service could make and try to establish which is the shortest overall route.
Show all of your working.

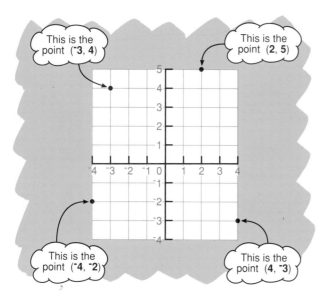

This is the point (⁻3, 4)

This is the point (2, 5)

This is the point (⁻4, ⁻2)

This is the point (4, ⁻3)

1 Write the coordinates of each of the points, A, B, C, D.

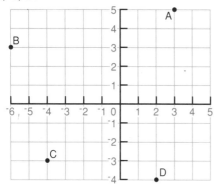

You need squared or graph paper.

2 Plot each of these points and label each one with the correct letter.

P (3, 6)   Q (⁻5, 4)   R (⁻2, ⁻7)   S (4, ⁻2)

3 (a) Plot each of the following points:
A (2, 0)   B (0, 2)   C (⁻2, 0)   D (0, ⁻2)
(b) Draw the shape ABCD.
(c) What is the shape ABCD?
(d) Find the area of ABCD.

4 (a) Plot the points A(3, 4) and B(⁻3, 0)
(b) Draw the line AB.
(c) Plot the points C(1, ⁻1) and D(⁻1, 2)
(d) Draw the line CD.
(e) Write the value of the angle between AB and CD.
(f) Estimate the angle between AB and the x-axis.
(g) Estimate the length of the line AB.

5 (a) Plot each of the following points
(10, 0)	(8, 6)	(6, 8)	(0, 10)
(⁻6, 8)	(⁻8, 6)	(⁻10, 0)	(⁻8, ⁻6)
(⁻6, ⁻8)	(0, ⁻10)	(6, ⁻8)	(8, ⁻6)

(b) Join the points with a smooth curve.
(c) What shape is the curve?

6 (a) Plot the points P, Q, R and S which have coordinates (3, ⁻3), (1, 2), (⁻4, 2) and (⁻2, ⁻3) respectively.
(b) Draw the shape PQRS.
(c) What is the shape PQRS?
(d) Find the area of PQRS.

7 (a) Plot the points A(3, 2) and B(⁻5, ⁻8)
(b) Draw the line AB.
(c) Write the coordinates of the mid-point of the line AB.
The line CD is perpendicular to AB. C is the point (2, ⁻6)
(d) Find possible coordinates for D.

You need a protractor and ruler.

8 (a) Plot the point A with coordinates (3, 4)
(b) Draw the line OA from the origin to A.
(c) Measure the length OA.
(d) Measure the angle between OA and the x-axis.

9 (a) Draw the line OP from the origin. The line makes an angle of 67° with the x-axis. The length of the line is 13 units.
(b) Write the approximate coordinates of P.

10 A line OA is 7 units long and makes an angle of 45° with the negative x-axis. Find the coordinates of A.

The angles marked **p** are equal.
They are **vertically opposite** angles.
The angles marked **q** are also equal and they are
also **vertically opposite**.

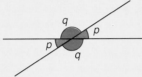

The angles **p** and **q** add up to 180°
That is **p + q = 180°**

1 Calculate each of the angles marked with a letter.

(a)

(b)

(c)

(d)

(e)

(f)

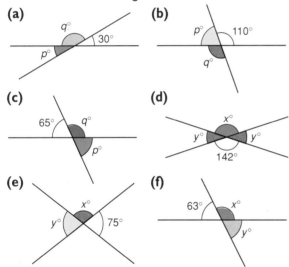

A line cuts across two parallel lines.
The angles marked with the same letter are equal.

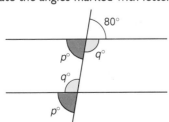

2 Calculate the angles marked with letters.

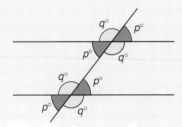

3 Calculate all the angles marked with a letter.

(a)   **(b)**

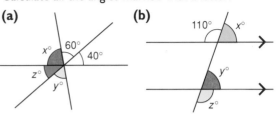

(c)   **(d)**

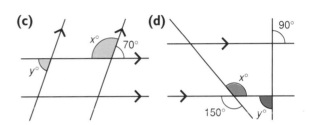

(e)   **(f)**

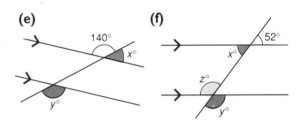

(g)   **(h)**

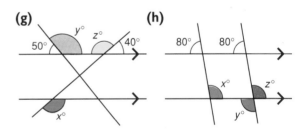

4 These diagrams have not been drawn accurately. The
information about the angles is correct.

(a)   **(b)**

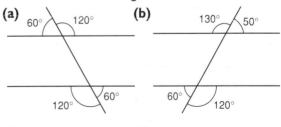

(c)   **(d)**

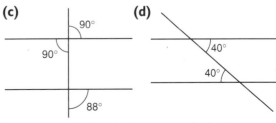

In each case decide whether or not the horizontal
lines can be parallel, and give an explanation.

The Seahorse Café

Kathy owns a cafe, which opens only at lunchtime. She wants to seek the **opinion** of her customers and potential customers about what they would **like to see on the menu.**

She decides to design a **questionnaire** to find out more.

A questionnaire should:
• ask questions
• not ask leading questions inviting particular responses
• be in a logical order
• provide tick answers.

Kathy designed this questionnaire.

Questionnaire

Q 1 What sex are you?

Male ☐

Female ☐

Q 2 What is your age?

0 – 15	
15 – 20	
20 – 30	
30 – 45	
45 – 65	
Over 65	

Q 3 What drinks would you like on the menu?

Fruit juice	
Squash	
Tea	
Coffee	
Milk	
Water	
Chocolate	
Carbonated drink	

Q 4 What snacks would you like on the menu?

Crisps	
Chocolate	
Biscuits	
Nuts	
Cake	
Buns	
Other	

1 Kathy used the questionnaire and found that fruit juice and carbonated drinks were very popular answers to Q3.
How could she improve the questionnaire to get more detailed information about this?

2 Why might Q2 be confusing to some people? Improve Q2.

3 In Q4 a lot of people ticked 'other'.
How could Kathy improve the questionnaire so that she knew what other items people wanted?

Kathy decided that she wanted to offer breakfast in the café.

4 Design a questionnaire which Kathy could use to survey opinion about breakfast choices.

5 Use the questionnaire you have designed to survey the opinion of 30 people.

6 Draw statistical diagrams that best show the results of your survey.
Choose from the following
Pictograms, Bar charts, Pie charts, Line graphs, Bar line graphs, Histograms

7 Use the statistical diagrams to help you advise Kathy of the food and drink she could offer at breakfast.

At a later date Kathy decides that she would like to open her café in the evenings.

8 Design a questionnaire for Kathy to use to survey opinion about evening meals and drinks.

9 Test the questionnaire on 30 people.

10 Draw statistical diagrams that best show the results of your survey.

11 Write a short report to Kathy advising her of what she should offer. Refer to your statistical diagrams for support and guidance.

There are 25 students in class 11M at Whatling High School. Sixteen of the students are girls, the remainder are boys. Mrs McInness, the form tutor, has to choose some students to do certain jobs.

She wants to be particularly fair in the way she selects students, because her daughter, Katy, is in the class. She writes each of their names on separate slips of paper, puts all of these slips of paper into a hat and pulls out one of the slips of paper.

1 How many boys are there in class 11M?

2 When Mrs McInness pulls a slip of paper out of the hat what is the probability that she will select:

(a) one with a girl's name on it
(b) one with a boy's name on it
(c) the one with Katy's name on it?

Write your answers as fractions.

3 Write your three answers to question **2** as:

(a) decimals   (b) percentages.

Using this process, Mrs McInness selects the following people.
Karen, Tracy, Mike, Billy and Jodie.
Their names are now no longer in the hat.

4 How many names are left in the hat?

Mrs McInness has one more name to select, so she dips into the hat for the last time and pulls out one slip of paper.

5 What is the probability that she will now select a slip of paper with:

(a) a girl's name on it   (b) a boy's name on it
(c) Katy's name on it?

Write your answers as fractions.

6 Write your answers to question **5** as:

(a) decimals   (b) percentages.

At lunch time class 11M play team games. They have formed five teams. These are labelled
Red Blue Green White Black

To see who will play who in the first match, Mrs McInness writes the words **Red, Blue, Green, White, Black** on five slips of paper.

She puts these slips of paper in a hat and then draws one out.

7 What is the probability that the first slip of paper will have Black written on it? Write your answer as a fraction.

The first slip of paper drawn out did have **Black** written on it. There are now only four slips of paper in the hat. A second slip is drawn out of the hat.

8 What is the probability that the second slip of paper will have **Red** written on it? Write your answer as a fraction.

9 Write your answers to questions **7** and **8** as:

(a) decimals   (b) percentages.

The first two teams drawn out of the hat were indeed **Black** and **Red**.

10 After selecting the first two teams. how many slips of paper are still in the hat?

Mrs McInness now selects a third slip of paper.

11 What is the probability that this slip of paper will have **Blue** written on it? Give your answer as a:

(a) fraction   (b) decimal to two decimal places
(c) percentage to the nearest whole number.

Katarina and her family, from Germany, are touring England, Scotland and Wales for their summer holiday. They have bought a road map. One of the pages has a mileage chart which shows the distances in miles between the major cities.

The chart shows that the distance between Manchester and Edinburgh is **219 miles**.

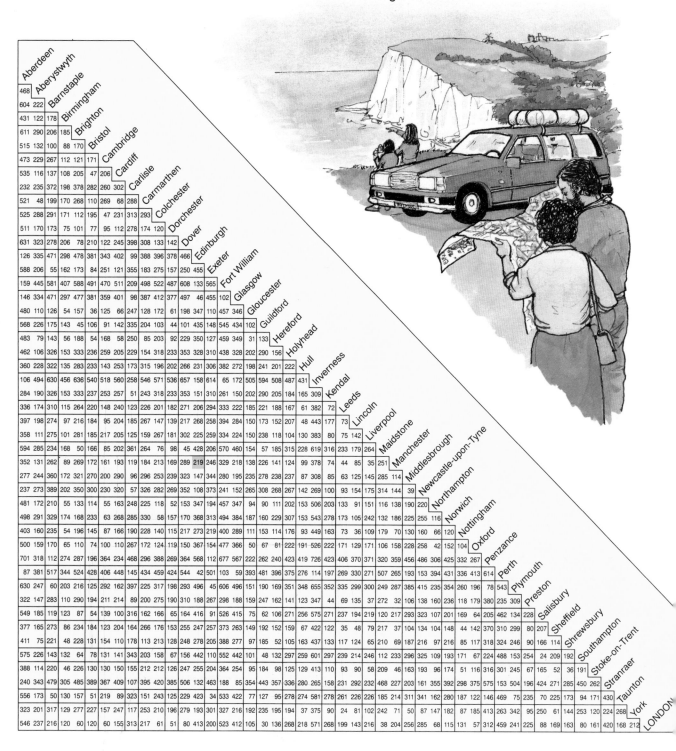

1 Use the table to find the distances between:

(a) London and Edinburgh

(b) Dover and Bristol

(c) Middlesbrough and Shrewsbury

(d) Cardiff and Norwich

(e) Oxford and Cambridge

(f) Inverness and Aberystwyth

(g) Leeds and Taunton

(h) Preston and York

(i) Glasgow and Stranraer

(j) Hereford and Colchester.

2 Name a town or city which is:

(a) 312 miles from London

(b) 59 miles from Glasgow

(c) 306 miles from Exeter

(d) 98 miles from Dorchester

(e) 51 miles from Taunton

(f) 407 miles from Birmingham

(g) 48 miles from Hull

(h) 120 miles from Nottingham

(i) 46 miles from Stoke-on-Trent

(j) 630 miles from Aberdeen.

3 Use the table to find:

(a) the town or city nearest to Manchester

(b) the town or city nearest to Glasgow

(c) the town or city furthest from Nottingham

(d) the town or city furthest from London

(e) the total distance from London to Oxford to Cambridge and straight back to London

(f) the total distance from Glasgow to Leeds to Norwich

(g) the total distance from Cardiff to Carmarthen then on to Aberystwyth then straight back to Cardiff

(h) the total distance from Birmingham to Sheffield to Lincoln to Nottingham and then straight back to Birmingham

(i) the distance from Newcastle to London and back

(j) the distance from Aberystwyth to London going via Norwich.

4 Use the table to work out:

(a) which two towns or cities are furthest apart and the distance between them

(b) the mean (average) distance of the towns or cities from London

(c) the mean distance of the towns or cities from Glasgow

(d) the mean distance of the towns or cities from Hull

(e) the two towns or cities nearest to each other, naming those towns or cities.

Katarina's family start their holiday by arriving on the ferry at Dover. They have a map on which they have drawn their holiday route.

5 (a) Calculate the total distance they will travel if they follow that route.

(b) Their car averages 32 miles per gallon of petrol. How many gallons of petrol will they use if they follow their planned route?

(c) They can expect to travel at an average speed of 40 miles per hour.
How many hours will they spend travelling if they follow their planned route?

Maybe, maybe not

Karen has bought her young brother, Robert, a game of Snakes and Ladders for Christmas.

When they play the game they roll a die.

The die can finish with any one of the six numbers
1, 2, 3, 4, 5, 6
showing on its top face. Each number has one chance in six of being the one on the top face.

This is written as
the probability of getting a 1 is $\frac{1}{6}$

Similarly the probability of getting a 2 is $\frac{1}{6}$

Probability can only be given as a fraction, decimal or percentage.

1 When they roll the die once, what is the probability of getting:

(a) a three   **(b)** a four   **(c)** a five   **(d)** a six?

Write your answers as fractions.

After they have finished playing Snakes and Ladders, Karen and her brother play a game of cards.
Karen shuffles the pack of 52 cards. She then deals one to her brother.

---

2 What is the probability that he will receive:

(a) a red card   **(b)** a heart
(c) a black card   **(d)** a spade
(e) the six of hearts   **(f)** the ten of spades
(g) an ace   **(h)** a red ace
(i) a king   **(j)** a picture card?

Write your answers as fractions.

3 The honour cards are the four jacks, four queens, four kings and four aces.
When Karen deals a card to her brother what is the probability that he will receive:

(a) an honour card   **(b)** a black honour card
(c) a heart that is an honour card?

On Christmas night Karen and her family sit down to watch television. They cannot decide which channel to watch. Karen's father suggests that they write

| BBC1 | BBC2 | ITV | Chan 4 |

on four slips of paper. They put their four slips of paper into a hat. Karen's mother then selects one of these slips of paper without looking (at random).

4 What is the probability that Karen's mother will select the slip of paper with the following written on it:
(a) BBC1   **(b)** Chan4   **(c)** ITV?

Write your answers as fractions.

On Boxing Day morning Karen and Robert play another game with two dice.

They have two dice, a black one and a white one. They roll the two dice and look at the outcome.
Three different possible outcomes are

Black	White
1	5
5	1
3	4

---

5 Show that when Karen and her brother roll the two dice there are a total of 36 different outcomes.
List all 36 outcomes.

6 When they roll the two dice, what is the probability that the outcome will be:

	Black	White
(a)	4	2
(b)	2	5
(c)	3	3

(d) a total score of   3,   12,   1,   8?

On her 10th birthday Jane's father gives her £20 as a present.

On each subsequent birthday he increases the amount he gives her by £5.

1 How much will she receive on her:

   (a) 15th birthday   **(b)** 20th birthday?

2 On which birthday should she receive £55?

3 Jane would like to draw a graph to show how much money she can expect to receive on all her birthdays from her 10th up to and including her 25th. Draw such a graph.

4 Calculate the total amount of money Jane should receive from her father by the time she is 25 years old.

5 Change the amount given to Jane by her father on her 10th birthday and the extra amount he gives her on each subsequent birthday.
Investigate the amounts she can expect to receive and the total amount she should receive as she gets older.

Show all of your working and explain all of your results.
Make and test any general statements.

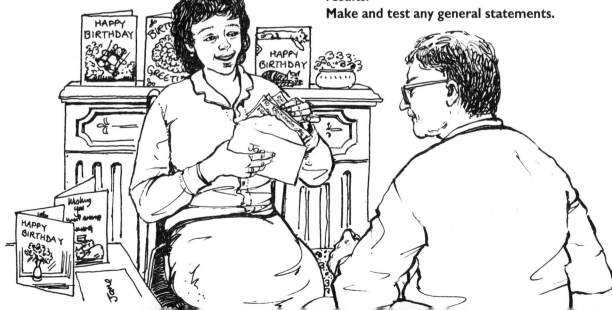

Seamus has drawn four dots in a square.

He has to join the four dots with straight lines.

Three different ways of doing so are

 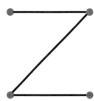

1   How many different ways can Seamus join the four dots using straight lines?

2   Draw a pattern of 5 dots as

     Investigate the number of different ways Seamus could join these 5 dots, again using straight lines.

3   Draw different patterns of dots.
     Change the number of dots.
     Investigate the number of different ways Seamus could join your dots, using straight lines.

Record the possible results.
Make and record any observations.
Make and test any general results.

Fiona McIntosh is setting out a new lawn.

The lawn is to be in the shape of a rectangle.
Two sides of the rectangle are a fence.
The other two sides are to be bordered by some paving slabs.
The paving slabs measure 1 metre by 1 metre.
One design she looks at is

Fiona realises that she will need 16 one metre square paving slabs to make this border for her 6 metre by 9 metre lawn.

1 How many 1 metre by 1 metre slabs would Fiona need to border the two sides of a lawn which measures:

(a) 5 m by 7 m

(b) 10 m by 10 m

(c) 12 m by 8 m

(d) any two measurements of your own choice?

2 **Investigate** the number of 1 m by 1 m paving slabs Fiona would require for lawns of various sizes.

3 **Investigate** the situation when not only the size of the lawn can vary but also the size of the paving slabs.

Hockey half-time

The hockey match between Whatling and Lawsall ended with the scores

     Whatling 2   Lawsall 2

Sue and Jan missed the match, but found out the final result.

I wonder what the half-time score was?

It could have been many things...

...it could have been
1 – 1
2 – 1
0 – 2
or many other scores.

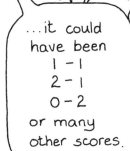

1 When a hockey match finishes with a score of **2 – 2**, show that there could have been **9** different possible half-time scores.

2 How many different possible half-time scores could there be for a hockey match that finishes with a score of:
    (a) 3 – 2   **(b)** 2 – 3   **(c)** 4 – 0   **(d)** 5 – 2?

3 **Investigate** the number of possible half-time scores for a hockey match which finishes with an even score.

Explain your answers.
Record your results and observations.
Make and test any general statements.

Hayley and David have been making the number 7 by addings 1s and 2s in several different ways.

Hayley has found
one way $7 = 2 + 2 + 2 + 1$

David has found
another $7 = 2 + 2 + 1 + 2$

A third is $7 = 1 + 1 + 1 + 1 + 1 + 1 + 1$

1. Show that the number 7 can be made by addings 1s and 2s in 21 different ways.

2. By adding 1s and 2s only, find the number of different ways of making:
   (a) 6   **(b)** 8
   (c) any two numbers of your choice.

3. **Investigate** the number of different ways of making any whole number by adding 1s and 2s only.

The number 7 can also be made in different ways by adding 2s and 3s.

One way is $7 = 2 + 2 + 3$

Another is $7 = 3 + 2 + 2$

4. Show that by addings 2s and 3s only, the number 7 can be made in only 3 different ways.

5. By adding only 2s and 3s, find the number of different ways of making:
   (a) 6   **(b)** 8
   (c) any two numbers of your choice.

6. Investigate the number of different ways of making any whole number by adding only 2s and 3s.

In your investigations show all of your work clearly.
Write down any comments or observations.
Try to give any general results with explanations or tests.

I Work out the value of:

(a) 3×2^2 (b) $(3 \times 2)^2$

(c) 3×2^4 (d) $(3 + 2)^3$

(e) $(5 + 4)^2$ (f) $3^3 - 8$

(g) $2^3 + 3^3$ (h) $1^3 + 2^3 + 3^3 + 4^3$

2 Harry has been given this problem 'Divide 36 by 2 until it cannot be divided equally by 2 any further . . .

$$2\,\lfloor\ 36$$
$$2\,\lfloor\ 18$$
$$\,\lfloor\ 9$$
$$\text{stop}$$

. . . now divide by 3 until you get an answer of I.'

$$3\,\lfloor\ 9$$
$$3\,\lfloor\ 3$$
$$\,\lfloor\ 1$$
$$\text{stop}$$

(a) How many times did Harry divide by • 2 • 3?

(b) Work out $2^2 \times 3^2$.

(c) What do you notice about your answer to (b)?

3 (a) Divide 72 by 2 until it cannot be divided equally by 2 any further.

(b) Continue to divide by 3 until you get an answer of I.

$$2\,\lfloor\ 72$$
$$2\,\lfloor\ $$
$$3\,\lfloor\ $$
$$3\,\lfloor\ $$
$$\,\lfloor\ 1$$
$$\text{stop}$$

(c) How many times did you divide by 2?

(d) How many times did you divide by 3?

(e) Work out $2^3 \times 3^2$.

(f) What do you notice about your answer?

4 (a) Divide 60 by 2 until the answer cannot be divided equally by 2 any further.

(b) Continue to divide by 3 until the answer cannot be divided equally by 3 any further.

(c) Continue to divide by 5 until you get an answer of I.

(d) Write how many times you divided by:
2, 3, 5

(e) Use what you found out in question 3 part (f) to check your answer. Show your working.

You need a calculator.

5 These workings show the number 1800 which has been divided by 2 then 3 then 5

(a) Write the numbers which can be used to check that the number has been divided correctly.

(b) Check that it is correct.

$$2\,\lfloor\ 1800$$
$$2\,\lfloor\ 900$$
$$2\,\lfloor\ 450$$
$$3\,\lfloor\ 225$$
$$3\,\lfloor\ 75$$
$$5\,\lfloor\ 25$$
$$5\,\lfloor\ 5$$
$$\,\lfloor\ 1$$
$$\text{stop}$$

6 (a) Work out the answer to this problem
$2^4 \times 3^2 \times 5^3$

(b) How many times can you divide your answer by 2?

(c) How many times can you continue to divide by 3?

(d) How many times can you continue to divide by 5?

7 Here is another division problem, without answers.

(a) Work out the number to be divided.

(b) Copy and complete the problem.

$$2\,\lfloor\ ?$$
$$5\,\lfloor\ ?$$
$$5\,\lfloor\ ?$$
$$5\,\lfloor\ ?$$
$$7\,\lfloor\ ?$$
$$\,\lfloor\ 1$$
$$\text{stop}$$

8 Divide each of these numbers by the instructions in the brackets until they cannot be divided equally any further, or until you get down to one. Check each number, showing your working.

(a)   84 (divide by 2 then 3 then 7)

(b) 108 (divide by 2 then 3)

(c) 100 (divide by 2 then 5)

(d) 135 (divide by 3 then 5)

(e) 875 (divide by 5 then 7)

(f) 1232 (divide by 2 then 7 then 11)

(g) 2520 (divide by 2 then 3 then 5 then 7)

1 Leanne and Natasha want to share these 15 counters between them. They know that 15 cannot be shared equally between two people, so they decide to share it in the ratio 1:2. This means that for every one Leanne takes, Natasha takes two.

  (a) How many counters are taken from the pile each round? (A round is one go each.)

  (b) How many rounds does it take before all the counters have gone?

  (c) How many counters does each girl get each time?

2 Paljit and Errol have a similar problem. They want to share 25 counters between them. They decide to share them in the ratio 3:2. This means that for every 3 Paljit takes, Errol takes 2.

  (a) How many counters are taken from the pile each round?

  (b) How many rounds does it take before all the counters have gone?

  (c) How many counters does each boy get?

3 Sandra, Joel and Esther open a packet of sweets and find that it contains 24 sweets. They decide to share them in the ratio 1:2:3

  (a) Explain what the ratio 1:2:3 means in this problem.

  (b) How many sweets are shared out each round?

  (c) How many rounds does it take to share out all the sweets?

  (d) How many sweets does each person get?

4 Ken and Sheila try to share 18 sweets in the ratio 3:5. What problem will they come across?

5 Write a sentence to explain:

  (a) £26 shared in the ratio 5:8

  (b) 26 bars of chocolate shared in the ratio 8:5

  (c) 27 sweets shared in the ratio 1:3:5

  (d) 20 counters shared in the ratio 1:2:2:5

  (e) £18 shared in the ratio 1:3:5

6 Solve the problems given in question 5.

This length of wood is 14 cm long. Kirstie is dividing the wood in the ratio 2:5. What fraction of the total length is the smaller piece?

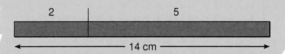

The smaller length will be 4 cm. The total length was 14 cm.

The fraction is $\frac{4}{14} = \frac{2}{7}$

7 What fraction of the total length of the wood is the larger piece? What do you notice about the two fractions?

8 What fraction of the original will the following be if:

  (a) a length of wood is divided in the ratio 1:2

  (b) a sum of money is shared in the ratio 4:9

  (c) a box of sweets is shared out in the ratio 2:3:7. Give the fractions in their lowest terms.

9 A length of pipe, 20 cm long, is to be divided in the ratio 2:3.

  (a) What fraction of the original length will the larger piece be?

  (b) How long will the larger piece be?

10 Sally, Mark and Brian want to share £30 in the ratio 2:3:5

  (a) Find what fraction of the £30:
    • Sally gets • Mark gets.

  (b) How much money does Brian get?

Percentages 3

1 Find:

(a) 230 ÷ 10   (b) 560 ÷ 10   (c) 34 ÷ 10

(d) 250 ÷ 100   (e) 870 ÷ 100   (f) 54 ÷ 100

(g) 25 ÷ 100   (h) 78 ÷ 100   (i) 4 ÷ 100

Duljit has been asked to find 24% of £26·50

$$24\% = 0{\cdot}24$$

As a decimal fraction $10\% = \frac{10}{100} = 0{\cdot}1$

As a decimal fraction $1\% = \frac{1}{100} = 0{\cdot}01$

Instead of finding 24% by adding:
10% + 10% + 1% + 1% + 1% + 1% = 24%

the same result can be obtained by adding:
0·1 + 0·1 + 0·01 + 0·01 + 0·01 + 0·01 = 0·24
so
24% of £26·50 = 0·24 × £26·50 = £6·36

2 If Duljit had been asked to find 34% of £6·36, by what decimal fraction should he multiply the £6·36?

3 Hazel wants to find 58% of 11·5 kg.

(a) By what should she multiply the 11·5 kg?

(b) What is 58% of 11·5 kg?

4 Find 32% of £64 by:

(a) finding 10% and multiplying by 3,
finding 1% and multiplying by 2
and adding the two answers together

(b) multiplying 64 by 0·32.

5 Write these percentages as decimal fractions:

(a) 25%   (b) 56%   (c) 62%   (d) 11%

(e) 70%   (f) 7%   (g) 12·5%   (h) 67·5%

6 Find:

(a) 42% of 6400 g   (b) 56% of 2 m

(c) 75% of 240 ml   (d) 5% of £2·46

(e) 16% of 1200 cm   (f) 8% of 10 mins

(g) 120% of 800 kg   (h) 150% of 86 p

7 In this packet of biscuits find the weight of:

(a) fat

(b) carbohydrates.

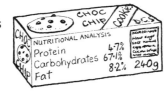

NUTRITIONAL ANALYSIS
Protein 4·7%
Carbohydrates 67·1%
Fat 8·2% 240g

1989 was known as the 'boom year' for house prices. Prices went up by an average of 24% during the year.

If this diagram represents the price of a house at the beginning of the year,

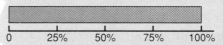

then this diagram represents the price at the end of the year.

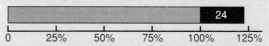

As a percentage the new value is
100% + 24% = 124% of the old value

8 Write these as a percentage of the old value if:

(a) a house increases in value by 16%

(b) a bank account increases by 11%

(c) the weight of a man goes up by 25%

(d) the value of a car goes up by 20%

(e) the value of a dishwasher increases by 44%

Tom earns £24 500 a year. If he gets a 15% increase, what will his new salary be?

As a percentage of his old salary his new salary is
100 + 15 = 115%
As a decimal fraction 115% = 1·15
Tom's new salary is 1·15 × £24 500 = £28 175

9 If you want to increase a quantity by 24% what do you multiply by?

10 If you want to increase an amount by 40% what do you multiply by?

11 Gail wants to increase her weight by 4%. What should she multiply her present weight by to find the weight she wants to be?

12 Increase:

(a) £120 by 20%   (b) 56 kg by 25%

(c) 2·4 m by 16%   (d) £1240 by 10·5%

(e) 126 cm by 2%

During 1992 house prices
fell by an average of 15%

If this diagram represents the price of a house at
the beginning of the year,

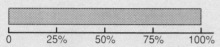

then this diagram represents the price at the end of
the year.

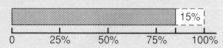

As a percentage the new value is
100% – 15% = 85% of the old value

13 Write these as a percentage of the old value if:

(a) a house decreases in value by 16%

(b) a bank account decreases by 11%

(c) the weight of a man goes down by 5%

(d) the value of a car goes down by 22%

14 If you want to decrease a quantity by 34% what do
you multiply by?

15 If you want to decrease an amount by 16% what do
you multiply by?

16 Alan decreases his weight by 4%. What should you
multiply by to find his new weight?

17 Decrease:

(a) £120 by 20%   (b) 56 kg by 25%

(c) 2·4 m by 16%   (d) £1240 by 10·5%

(e) 126 cm by 2%

18 The number of pupils at Eastgrove School fell by
24%. If the school had 1250 pupils before the fall,
how many does it have now?

19 Tom went to the casino to play roulette. At the
beginning of the evening he had £600.
Unfortunately, he was very unlucky and lost 45% of
his money. How much money did he lose?

20 A television set costs £540 plus VAT. Find the total
price if VAT is:

(a) 10%   (b) 15%   (c) 17·5%

21 Anna invests £1000 in a savings account on the
1st January 1994. The interest paid is 8% per annum.

(a) What do you multiply by to find the amount
she will have at the end of the first year?

(b) How much money did she have in her account
at the end of the first year?

(c) Copy and complete this table. Give the
amounts to the nearest £.

Date	Amount
1/1/94	£1000
1/1/95	
1/1/96	
1/1/97	
1/1/98	

22 A car which cost £12 000 new depreciates by

15% in its first year

10% in its second year

8% each year thereafter.

(a) Find the value of the car after one year.

(b) Copy and complete this table giving your
answers to the nearest £.

Value	£
new	12 000
after 1 year	
after 2 years	
after 3 years	
after 4 years	
after 5 years	

23 An investment account increases by 8% in the first
year and a further 6% in the second.

(a) What should you multiply by to find the value
after the first year?

(b) What should you multiply by to find the value
after two years? (Be careful, it is **not** 1·14)

24 A house increases in value by 15% in one year. The
following year its value falls by 10%. What is the
percentage change after two years?

Reg and Joyce inherit £3000 in their uncle's will.
The money is to be shared in the ratio 3:2.
How much does each receive?

Reg's share will be $\frac{3}{5}$

Joyce's share will be $\frac{2}{5}$

Reg receives $\frac{3}{5}$ of £3000 = £1800

Joyce receives $\frac{2}{5}$ of £3000 = £1200

           check £3000

1 Danny and Cher share 56 fireworks in the ratio 1:3
  (a) What fraction of the fireworks does Danny receive?
  (b) How many fireworks does he get?
  (c) What fraction does Cher receive?
  (d) How many does she get?

2 Abdul and Jarling serve food in a café. Abdul works 5 days a week and Jarling 3 days. To be fair, they agree to share their tips in the ratio of the number of days they work.
  (a) If the tips in one week came to £32, how much should Jarling receive?
  (b) The following week the tips came to £42·72, how much should Abdul receive?

3 In a GCSE mathematics course, 80 marks are for the final examination papers and 20 marks for coursework assignments.
  (a) Write the ratio of exam marks to coursework marks in its simplest form.
  (b) Natalie obtains a total of 76 marks. If she gained three times as many marks for her final exam as for her coursework, how many coursework marks did she gain?

4 Tracey, Aneal and Jaime share a prize of £800. They agree to share this money in the ratio 1:3:4
  (a) What fraction does Tracey receive?
  (b) What fraction do Tracey and Jaime receive between them?
  (c) How much does Aneal receive?

5 At a coffee morning a total of £350 was raised. £250 came from selling raffle tickets and the rest from selling coffee.
  (a) What is the ratio of the amount raised from the raffle to the amount raised by selling coffee?
  (b) The following year a second coffee morning raised £558. If the money raised was in the same ratio as in the previous year, how much was raised from selling coffee?

6 Barry is making some orange squash to sell at the school fete.
  (a) How much orange does he need to make 6 litres of squash?
  (b) How much water will Barry need to make 10 litres of squash?

ORANGE SQUASH
Add 4 litres of water to 1 litre of concentrated Orange squash. Stir and serve

7 In one month during the cricket season the school team scored 640 runs. These were all scored by the four best batsmen, in the ratio 3:4:4:5

  (a) How many runs did the top scorer make?
  (b) What was the difference between the number of runs scored by the top scorer and the lowest scorer?

8 In Eastgrove School the ratio of pupils to teachers is 18·2 : 1
  (a) Multiply 18·2 by 5
  (b) Rewrite the ratio in whole numbers.
  (c) What is the smallest possible number of pupils in the school?
  (d) If the actual number of teachers and pupils was 1152, how many teachers were there?

In a sale at Imelda's there is $\frac{1}{3}$ off all marked prices.

Gaynor buys a dress. How much does she have to pay in the sale?

If this diagram represents the normal cost,

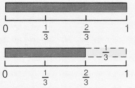

then this diagram represents the sale price.

As a fraction, the sale price must be

$1 - \frac{1}{3} = \frac{2}{3}$ **of the original price.**

1 Write the sale price as a fraction of the original price if:

(a) a $\frac{1}{4}$ discount is given

(b) a $\frac{1}{5}$ reduction is given

(c) the price is reduce by $\frac{3}{8}$

(d) the price is reduced by $\frac{1}{2}$

(e) the sale notice reads $\frac{3}{10}$ off all goods.

2 At Whitegoods Leon reduces all his prices by $\frac{1}{4}$. How much does he charge for:

(a) a washing machine originally costing £504

(b) a computer originally costing £1248

(c) a compact disc player originally costing £356?

The price of certain goods is increased by $\frac{1}{4}$

If this diagram represents the original price

then this diagram represents the new price.

As a fraction, the new price is

$1 + \frac{1}{4} = 1\frac{1}{4}$ **of the old price.**

3 What fraction would you multiply by if an item is:

(a) increased by $\frac{1}{3}$

(b) increased by $\frac{2}{5}$

(c) reduced by $\frac{3}{7}$?

4 In Ambletown there are two electrical shops. They both sell Sunny video cameras for £780. On January 1st:
Nixons increases the selling price by $\frac{1}{8}$
Curies increases the selling price by 10%

(a) Calculate the new selling price charged by both shops.

(b) Which shop represents the best buy?

5 Which of these represents the best buy?

6 A new housing estate is built next to Eastgrove School and the number of pupils at the school increases by $\frac{3}{8}$

(a) By what number must you multiply to find the new total number of pupils?

(b) What is the decimal equivalent of this number?

(c) What is the percentage equivalent?

7 Which of these is the largest?

£100 increased by $\frac{2}{5}$ £120 increased by 12%

£180 reduced by $\frac{1}{4}$ £200 decreased by $\frac{1}{3}$

8 To combat rising costs, Browntrees decide they must either increase the cost of a Moorish Delight bar by $\frac{1}{5}$ or decrease the weight by $\frac{1}{5}$. As the manufacturer what would be your decision and why?

9 What is the overall effect of increasing an item by 10%, then reducing this increased amount by $\frac{1}{4}$?

Use the graph to answer questions **1** to **4**.

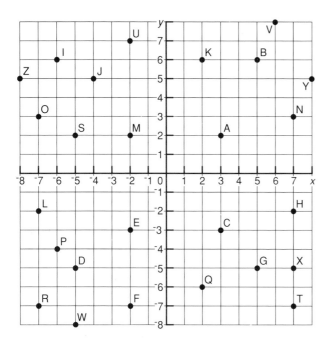

4 (a) Write three names of your own, with the negative signs where necessary, but with the order jumbled up, and then pass them to a friend. Ask your friend to try to work out the names.

(b) Now write three names, without any negative signs, but in the right order. Pass them to a friend to work out.

You need squared paper.

5 The triangle ABC has been reflected in the *x*-axis to give triangle A'B'C'

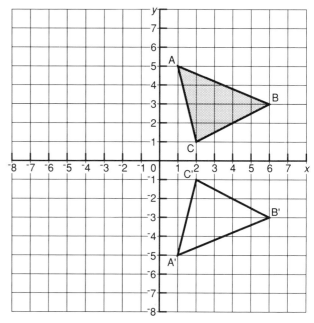

1 Each of these spells a word. What is each word?
   (a) (⁻7, ⁻7) (⁻2, ⁻3) (3, 2) (⁻7, ⁻2)
   (b) (2, ⁻6) (⁻2, 7) (⁻6, 6) (3, ⁻3) (2, 6)
   (c) (7, ⁻7) (⁻7, ⁻7) (3, 2) (⁻6, 6) (7, 3)
   (d) (⁻6, ⁻4) (⁻7, 3) (⁻5, ⁻8) (⁻2, ⁻3) (⁻7, ⁻7)
   (e) (7, ⁻7) (⁻2, ⁻3) (3, 2) (3, ⁻3) (7, ⁻2) (⁻2, ⁻3) (⁻7, ⁻7)

2 The letters of these names have been jumbled up.
   Find the name of a person by rearranging the letters.
   (a) (⁻2, 2) (2, 6) (⁻7, ⁻7) (3, 2)
   (b) (3, 2) (⁻7, ⁻2) (8, 5) (⁻7, ⁻2) (⁻5, 2)
   (c) (⁻2, ⁻3) (⁻7, ⁻7) (7, ⁻7) (⁻5, 2) (⁻2, ⁻3) (7, ⁻2)
   (d) (3, 2) (7, 3) (7, ⁻7) (⁻5, 2) (⁻6, 6) (⁻4, 5)

3 Here are some more names, but the person who wrote in the names forgot to put in the negative signs. For example (5, 6) could be (⁻5, 6) or (5, ⁻6) or (⁻5, ⁻6) or even (5, 6)
   (a) (7, 7) (7, 3) (2, 2)
   (b) (4, 5) (7, 3) (2, 3) (7, 2)
   (c) (7, 2) (2, 3) (7, 7) (7, 3) (8, 5)
   (d) (5, 8) (2, 3) (7, 3) (5, 5) (8, 5)
   (e) (5, 2) (3, 2) (7, 3) (5, 5) (7, 7) (3, 2)

(a) Write the coordinates of A', B' and C'
(b) On squared paper make a copy of the diagram.
(c) On your copy of the diagram show the image of triangle ABC after a reflection in the *y*-axis. Label this triangle A", B" and C".
(d) Write the coordinates of A", B" and C"

6 (a) On your copy of the diagram used in question **5** plot these points
   X(⁻1, ⁻5), Y(⁻6, ⁻3) and Z(⁻2, ⁻1) and join them up to make a triangle.

(b) Describe the reflection that maps triangle A'B'C' onto triangle XYZ.

7 (a) Make a copy of this diagram on squared paper.

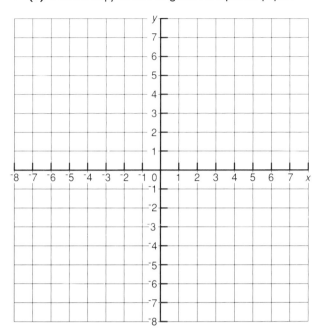

(b) Copy this table, plot and mark the six points on your diagram.

Point	Location	Image
A	(6, 3)	
B	(2, 3)	
C	(0, 4)	
D	(⁻1, 2)	
E	(⁻4, ⁻3)	
F	(⁻8, ⁻6)	

(c) Reflect each point in the *x*-axis and complete the table by writing in the coordinate points of each image.

(d) What is the relationship between the coordinates of a point and the coordinates of its image point?

8 A point (⁻6, 12) is reflected in the *x*-axis.
Without drawing, write the coordinates of the image.

9 Triangle ABC has coordinates (3, 2) (⁻2, 6) and (⁻4, ⁻7). The triangle is reflected in the *x*-axis.
Write the coordinates of the image triangle A'B'C'

10 (a) Make another copy of the diagram in question **7**.
The coordinate point A is (4, 2). These two numbers are added to give an answer of 6
4 + 2 = 6

(b) Write 4 more coordinates whose *x* and *y* numbers add up to 6.

(c) Plot the 5 points and join them with a straight line extended in both directions.

(d) Which of these points lie on the straight line? (⁻2, 8), (⁻3, 6), (7, ⁻1)

11 (a) Find 5 more coordinate points whose *x* number + *y* number equal ⁻6
(⁻2, ⁻4) is (⁻2 + ⁻4 = ⁻6)

(b) Plot these points on the same diagram and join them up with a straight line extended in both directions.

12 (a) Find 5 more coordinate points whose *x* number − *y* number equals 2
(5, 3) is (5 − 3 = 2)

(b) Plot these points on the same diagram and join them with a straight line extended in both directions.

(c) Write the coordinates of the two points where the three lines cross.

The Bermuda Triangle

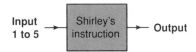

1 These are the first four triangular numbers.

1
3
6
10

(a) Copy and complete.

Position	Triangular number
1st	1
2nd	3
3rd	6
4th	10
5th	
6th	
7th	

(b) What is the 10th triangular number?

2 This flow diagram can be used to generate triangular numbers.

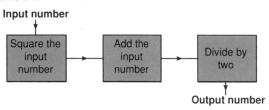

Input number →
Square the input number → Add the input number → Divide by two
→ Output number

Input number	1	2	3	4
Output number	1	3	6	10

(a) Use the flow diagram to check your answer to question **1 (b)**.

(b) What is the 12th triangular number?

(c) What is the 50th triangular number?

3 (a) Find:
- the 19th triangular number
- the 20th triangular number.

(b) Explain why the number 200 cannot be a triangular number.

4 Using a trial and improvement method find out whether the number 3081 is a triangular number. Show all your working.

3081
?

5 Shirley thinks she has found another flow diagram to generate triangular numbers.

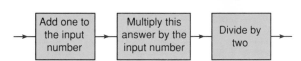

Add one to the input number → Multiply this answer by the input number → Divide by two →

(a) Work out the output sequence using Shirley's instructions for this flow diagram.

Input 1 to 5 → Shirley's instruction → Output

(b) Are triangular numbers being generated?

6 (a) Work out the 25th triangular number using the first set of instructions in question **2**.

(b) Work out the 25th triangular number using Shirley's instructions.

(c) Do you get the same answer?

7 (a) Copy and complete.

Position	Pattern A	Pattern B	Numbers generated
1st	$1^2 + 1$	1×2	2
2nd	$2^2 + 2$		
3rd	$3^2 + 3$	3×4	
4th		4×5	
5th			
6th			
7th			
8th			

(b) What is the connection between the sequence of numbers generated and the triangular numbers?

8 Alan and Shirley are having an argument.

I think that the number 3480 is a triangular number.

Of course it isn't!

Who do you agree with and why?

Kulbinder has been given this set of numbers.

1, 2, 3, 4

She has been asked to draw a diagram to show the effect of multiplying each number by 2 and adding 1

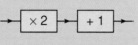

Kulbinder draws this diagram.

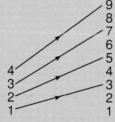

This is a **mapping diagram.**

1 (a) Work out the output from this flow diagram.

Input 1 to 4 → ×3 → −2 →

(b) Copy and complete this mapping diagram to show the same information.

2 Draw mapping diagrams to show the input and output of these flow diagrams.

(a) Input 2 to 5 → +3 → ×2 →

(b) Input 3 to 7 → −3 → ×3 →

(c) Input 4 to 8 → ×2 → −8 →

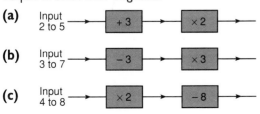

It is not always practical to draw full number lines, so the diagrams can be 'shortened' to

4 ——→ 8
3 ——→ 6
2 ——→ 4
1 ——→ 2
0 ——→ 0

3 Draw mapping diagrams to show:

(a) Input 2 to 6 → ×6 → −3 →

(b) Input 3 to 6 → +2 → ×4 →

(c) Input 2 to 8 step 2 → ÷2 → −1 →

(d) Input 0 to 6 step 2 → +4 → ÷2 →

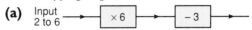

Mapping diagrams can also be used to show negative numbers.

This flow diagram has negative numbers in both its input and output.

Input ⁻2 to 1 → ×2 → −3 → ⁻7, ⁻5, ⁻3, ⁻1

The mapping diagram is

1 ——→ ⁻1
0 ——→ ⁻3
⁻1 ——→ ⁻5
⁻2 ——→ ⁻7

4 Draw mapping diagrams for:

(a) Input ⁻2 to 2 → ×2 → +3 →

(b) Input ⁻3 to 1 → +4 → ×3 →

(c) Input ⁻4 to 0 → take away from 6 →

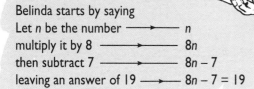

Let n be the number

Belinda has been asked to write this problem in 'maths shorthand':

A number is multiplied by 8 and then 7 is subtracted. This leaves an answer of 19

Belinda starts by saying
Let n be the number ⟶ n
multiply it by 8 ⟶ $8n$
then subtract 7 ⟶ $8n - 7$
leaving an answer of 19 ⟶ $8n - 7 = 19$

When Belinda had written the problem in maths shorthand she was asked to find the unknown number.

The problem to solve is $\qquad 8n - 7 = 19$

Start by writing
'something take away 7 equals 19' $\boxed{} - 7 = 19$

the something must be $\boxed{26} - 7 = 19$

this means that $\qquad 8n = 26$

so $\qquad n = \dfrac{26}{8}$

$\qquad n = 3 \cdot 25$

1 Write each of these in maths shorthand:

(a) A number is multiplied by 5 and 3 added. This leaves an answer of 18

(b) If you multiply a number by 5 and then subtract 3 you are left with 42

(c) Four times a certain number add 15 equals 47

(d) Add 4 to a number that you have multiplied by 7 to get 50

(e) If you take 4 away from a number you are left with 12

(f) If you take a certain number away from 4 you are left with 12

2 Explain, to your teacher or to a friend, the meaning of these equations:

(a) $4n + 5 = 6$ (b) $7n - 4 = 20$
(c) $7 - 4n = 59$ (d) $3n - 3 = {}^-40$
(e) $6n - 12 = 56$ (f) $5 + 3n = 12$
(g) $n - 7 = {}^-25$ (h) $7 - n = {}^-5$

3 What is the connection between the equation $4n = 18$ and the square?

n — Perimeter = 18 cm

4 Write a statement, in maths shorthand, that involves the perimeter of this rectangle.

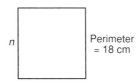

$2n$

5

Perimeter = 25 cm

5 Find the missing number from the box.

(a) $\boxed{} + 6 = 14$ (b) $\boxed{} + 5 = 19$
(c) $\boxed{} - 6 = 20$ (d) $\boxed{} - 8 = 14$
(e) $5 + \boxed{} = 3$ (f) $12 - \boxed{} = 5$
(g) $6 - \boxed{} = {}^-2$ (h) $\boxed{} - 8 = {}^-2$

6 Find the number, n in:

(a) $4n = 10$ (b) $2n = 11$
(c) $5n = 22$ (d) $3n = 10 \cdot 5$
(e) $6n = 14 \cdot 4$ (f) $4n = 0$
(g) $5n = {}^-6$ (h) $7n = {}^-50 \cdot 75$
(i) ${}^-2n = 10 \cdot 6$ (j) ${}^-4n = {}^-18$

7 Solve these equations by finding the number, n.

(a) $4n + 6 = 22$ (b) $5n - 4 = 36$
(c) $7 + 2n = 20$ (d) $4n - 8 = 10$
(e) $5n - 12 = 26$ (f) $6n + 20 = 47$
(g) $2n + 10 = 6$ (h) $3n - 10 = {}^-1$
(i) $6n + 29 = 11$ (j) $5n + 20 = {}^-10$
(k) $4 - 5n = {}^-8$ (l) $20 + 4n = {}^-15$

8 Find the lengths of each side of this triangle.

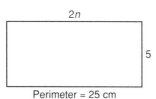

$n + 5$

$n - 1$

Perimeter = 25·5 cm

$n + 2$

The instructions for mapping diagrams are usually given using symbols.

The instruction $n \longrightarrow 2n + 3$ is the shorthand way of writing:

'Multiply a number by 2 then add 3'

or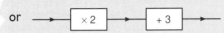

The mapping diagram for this instruction for the $n \longrightarrow 3n - 2$ set of numbers (2, 3, 4, 5)

means

'Multiply the input numbers by 3 then subtract 2'

or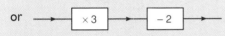

And this is the mapping diagram.

5 ———→ 11
4 ———→ 13
3 ———→ 9
2 ———→ 7

1 Draw mapping diagrams to show:

(a) $n \longrightarrow n - 2$ (3, 4, 5, 6, 7)
(b) $n \longrightarrow 5 - n$ (2, 3, 4, 5, 6)
(c) $n \longrightarrow 4n + 6$ ($^-$1, 0, 1, 2, 3)
(d) $n \longrightarrow n^2$ (1, 2, 3, 4)
(e) $n \longrightarrow n^2 + n$ (0, 2, 4, 6)

The arrow lines on a mapping diagram do not always map to different numbers.

The mapping diagram for $n \longrightarrow n^2$ ($^-$2, $^-$1, 0, 1, 2) is like this

2 ———→ 4
1 ———→ 1
0 ———→ 0
$^-$1
$^-$2

2 Draw mapping diagrams to show:

(a) $\longrightarrow n^2$ ($^-$3, $^-$2, $^-$1, 0, 1,)
(b) $\longrightarrow n^2 - 3$ ($^-$2, $^-$1, 0, 1, 2)
(c) $\longrightarrow n^2 + n$ ($^-$2, $^-$1, 0, 1, 2)
(d) $\longrightarrow n^2 - 3n$ ($^-$4, $^-$3, $^-$2, $^-$1, 0)

Gavin has been given this mapping diagram and asked to work out its instructions.

4 ———→ 7
3 ———→ 5
2 ———→ 3
1 ———→ 1
n ———→ ?

This means he has to find a 'rule' that works for all the input numbers.

Gavin notices that with $2 \longrightarrow 3$ the rule could be

$n \longrightarrow n + 1$ or $n \longrightarrow 2n - 1$

Check $n \longrightarrow n + 1$

This rule only works with the input, 2. It does not work for the other input numbers.

Check $n \longrightarrow 2n - 1$

This rule works for all the input numbers

4 ———→ $(2 \times 4) - 1 = 7$
3 ———→ $(2 \times 3) - 1 = 5$
2 ———→ $(2 \times 2) - 1 = 3$
1 ———→ $(2 \times 1) - 1 = 1$

The rule for the mapping is $n \longrightarrow 2n - 1$

3 Work out the rule for each of these mapping diagrams. Write your rule in the form $\boldsymbol{n} \rightarrow \square$

(a) 4 ——→ 6
    3 ——→ 5
    2 ——→ 4
    1 ——→ 3

(b) 2 ——→ 4
    1 ——→ 2
    0 ——→ 0
   $^-$1 ——→ $^-$2
   $^-$2 ——→ $^-$4

(c) 3 ——→ 10
    2 ——→ 7
    1 ——→ 4
    0 ——→ 1

(d) 3 ——→ 1
    2 ——→ 0
    1 ——→ $^-$1
    0 ——→ $^-$2

(e) 4 ——→ 2
    3 ——→ 3
    2 ——→ 4
    1 ——→ 5
    0 ——→ 6

(f) 5 ——→ 3·5
    4 ——→ 3
    3 ——→ 2·5
    2 ——→ 2
    1 ——→ 1·5
    0 ——→ 1·0

In real life

Daniel's father, Matthew, is an architect. When he draws a plan of a house he needs to make a **scale drawing**. This is one of his scale drawings of a new house.

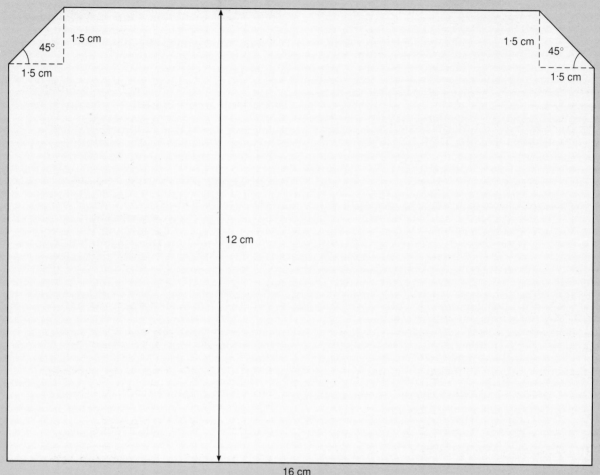

The real life house will be 16 metres wide.
Matthew has used **a scale of 1 centimetre to represent 1 metre**, so his drawing is only 16 cm wide.

The real life height of the house is 12 metres, so his scale drawing is only 12 cm high.

1 The back garden of the house Matthew is designing will be a rectangle measuring 16 m by 10 m.
Using a scale of 1 cm to represent 1 m, make a scale drawing of the back garden.

2 Matthew is also designing an office block.
The front of this block will be a rectangle 50 m high and 30 m wide.
Using a scale of 1 cm to represent 10 m, make a scale drawing of the front of the office block.

3 A building plot is in the shape of a right-angled triangle ABC. AB = 300 m, BC = 400 m and the angle at A is 90°.
   (a) Using a scale of 2 cm to represent 100 m, make a scale drawing of the building plot.
   (b) Measure the length of AC on your diagram.
   (c) Work out the real life length of AC on the plot.

4 Make a scale drawing of your classroom.
State what scale you use.

Trish has two rectangles.

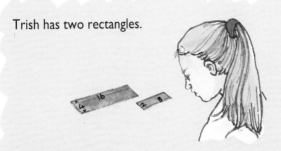

She notices that the blue rectangle is twice as big as the red one.
That is, the lengths of the sides of the blue rectangle are twice the lengths of the sides of the red one.

She finds a third rectangle which is green.

The green rectangle is three times as big as the red one. It is also one and a half times as big as the blue one.

The red, blue and green rectangles are **similar**. The word similar means that the rectangles look the same. Their sides are in the **same proportion** but they are of different sizes.

Trish can check that they are similar by doing three simple divisions. For each rectangle she works out the sum

> length of rectangle ÷ width of rectangle

Trish works out her results.

	Red rectangle	Blue rectangle	Green rectangle
Length	8	16	24
Width	2	4	6
Divide	4	4	4

When she does the division she gets **4** in every case. Because all these answers **are the same** it means that the three rectangles are similar.

1 Confirm that the three rectangles in the panel above, which are accurately drawn, are similar.

Here are two similar rectangles.

To calculate the width of the larger rectangle

length of the larger rectangle
> = 4 × length of the smaller one
so width of larger rectangle
> = 4 × width of the smaller one
> = 4 × 5 = 20 cm

2 Here are two pairs of similar rectangles. Calculate the length of the side marked with ?

(a)
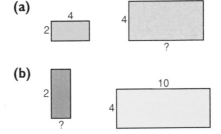

(b)

3 ABCD and PQRS are two similar rectangles.
AB = CD = 5 cm   BC = AD = 3 cm
PQ = RS = 30 cm
Calculate the lengths of QR and PS.

4 ABCD and PQRS are two similar rectangles.
AB = CD = 6 cm   BC = CD = 4 cm
PQ = RS = 15 cm
Calculate the lengths of QR and PS.

5 STUV and WXYZ are two similar rectangles.
WX = YZ = 12 cm   XY = WZ = 15 cm
ST = UV = 4 cm.
Calculate the lengths of TU and SV.

6 ▶ **Do Worksheet 5.**

7 How many of the smaller rectangles will be needed to completely fill the space inside the larger one?

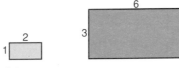

Explain your answer.

Areas of triangles

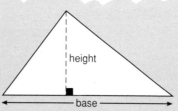

The area of any triangle is given by the formula

$$\text{Area} = \frac{\text{base} \times \text{height}}{2}$$

or $\quad A = \dfrac{bh}{2}$

This is because the area of the triangle is **half the area of the surrounding rectangle**.

1 Calculate the area of each of these triangles.

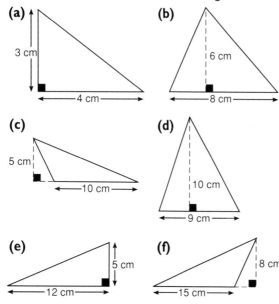

The **base** does not always have to be the bottom side of the triangle, but **the base and height must be at right angles**.

2 Calculate the area of each of these triangles.

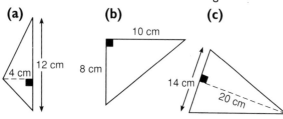

3 These are the bases and heights of some triangles. Calculate the area of each triangle.

  (a) base = 5 cm   height = 6 cm
  (b) base = 12 cm   height = 4 cm
  (c) base = 15 cm   height = 10 cm
  (d) base = 14 cm   height = 9 cm
  (e) base = 11 cm   height = 7 cm
  (f) base = 3·6 cm   height = 4·8 cm
  (g) base = 4·5 cm   height = 3·2 cm

When you know the area and base of a triangle you can calculate the height by using the formula

$$\text{height} = \frac{2 \times \text{Area}}{\text{base}}$$

and in a similar way

$$\text{base} = \frac{2 \times \text{Area}}{\text{height}}$$

4 (a) The area of a triangle is 20 cm^2 and its height is 4 cm. Calculate its base length.

  (b) The base of a triangle is 5 cm and its area is 30 cm^2. Calculate the height of the triangle.

  (c) The height of a triangle is 12 cm and its area is 42 cm^2. Calculate the length of the base of the triangle.

  (d) The area of a triangle is 64 cm^2. The length of the base of the triangle is 16 cm. Calculate the height of the triangle.

5 The area of this right-angled triangle is 32 cm^2. The base and height of the triangle are equal, and written as x cm. Calculate the value of x.

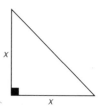

6 A builder measures out a triangular plot, ABC. The length of AB is 30 m and the perpendicular distance from C to AB is 20 m.

  (a) Sketch a plan of this plot.

  (b) Calculate the area of the plot.

7 In a triangle, PQR, PQ = 12 cm and the perpendicular distance from R to PQ is 7 cm. Calculate the area of the triangle.

A prism is a solid shape.
It has a base and top face which are identical.
Its cross-section is always the same.
The edges running from the base to the top face
are all straight lines.

These are three different prisms.

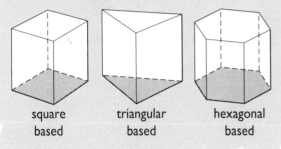

square   triangular   hexagonal
based   based   based

1▶ Do Worksheet 6.

2▶ Do Worksheet 7.

3 Each real life object has been labelled with a letter.

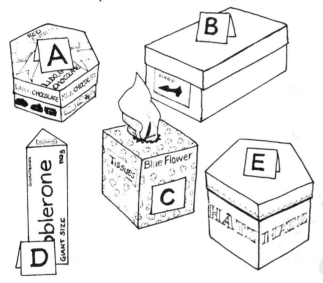

○ square based prism   ○ triangular based prism
○ hexagonal based prism ○ pentagonal based prism
○ rectangular, but not square, based prism

Match the correct letter to each geometrical name.

A prism with a rectangular base is called a **cuboid**.
When all the sides of a cuboid are of equal length it
is called a **cube**.

This is a square based
pyramid.

Every pyramid has a flat base and the edges from
this base meet at a point.

Here are three other pyramids.

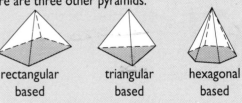

rectangular   triangular   hexagonal
based   based   based

4 Draw a sketch of:

  (a) a pyramid with a pentagon as its base

  (b) an octagonal based pyramid.

A triangular based pyramid has a special name.
It is called a **tetrahedron**.

5 Give at least one real life object which is in the
shape of:

  (a) a cuboid   **(b)** a cube

  (c) a triangular based prism

  (d) a square based pyramid

  (e) a triangular based pyramid.

These are the cross-sections of two solid shapes.

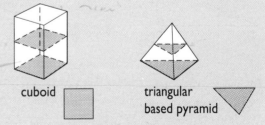

cuboid   triangular
                          based pyramid

A cross-section is formed by slicing the solid
parallel to its base, or one of the other faces in the
case of a prism.

6 Sketch the cross-section of:

  (a) a square based pyramid

  (b) a pentagonal based prism

  (c) any named shape of your own choosing.

Volumes

The **volume of a cuboid** is given by the formula
volume = area of base × height

The area of the base = length of base × width of base

or   area of base   = length × width

So **volume = length × width × height**

or

$\mathbf{V = l \times w \times h}$ or $\mathbf{V = lwh}$

To calculate the volume of a cuboid

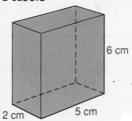

$V = l \times w \times h$
$V = 5 \times 2 \times 6$
$V = 10 \times 6$
$V = 60$ cubic centimetres
$\mathbf{V = 60 \ cm^3}$

6 cm

2 cm   5 cm

1 All these cuboids are measured in centimetres.
   Calculate the volume of each cuboid.

(a)

10
4   3

(b)
4
5   7

(c)
8
6   6

(d)

11
5   9

(e)
10
4   7

(f)
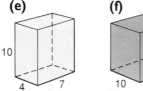
15
10   12

2 Calculate the volume of a cuboid which has these
   measurements
   length = 6 cm   width = 5 cm   height = 12 cm

3 Questions **(a)** — **(h)** give the measurements of a
   cuboid. All measurements are in centimetres, unless
   otherwise stated.
   Calculate the volume of each cuboid.

	length	width	height
(a)	3	5	2
(b)	4	10	3
(c)	8	4	6
(d)	12	10	8
(e)	15 m	0·4 m	5 m
(f)	0·6 m	1 m	30 cm
(g)	0·5 m	0·5 m	0·4 m
(h)	0·8 m	0·5 m	12 cm

4 Calculate the volume of a cube with sides:
   (a) 4 cm   **(b)** 3 cm   **(c)** 5 cm   **(d)** 10 cm

To calculate the height of a cuboid
The volume of a cuboid is 120 cm^3
The length of the cuboid is 5 cm and its width is 4 cm.

$V = l \times w \times h$
$120 = 5 \times 4 \times h$
$120 = 20 \times h$

so $20 \times h = 120$
$h = 120 \div 20$
$\mathbf{h = 6 \ cm}$

5 Copy and complete the table for cuboids.

V (cm³)	l (cm)	w (cm)	h (cm)
150	3	5	
120	6	5	
1000	10		10
8		1	2
200	5		10
162	6	9	
105	5		3

6 The diagram shows a cuboid.

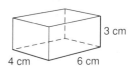

3 cm

4 cm   6 cm

The lengths of the sides of a second cuboid are double
the lengths of the first cuboid.
(a) Write the lengths of the sides of the second cuboid.
(b) Calculate the volume of the second cuboid.

To calculate the length of a side of a cube
The volume of a cube is 64 cm^3

You can work this out on your calculator.

Input **64** Press **2nd (or inv)** **$^x\sqrt{y}$** **3** **=**

Your calculator should now give a result of **4**

Ask your teacher for help if you do not get 4.

7 Calculate the lengths of the sides of a cube, with
volume in cm^3, of:

(a) 125   (b) 343   (c) 1000
(d) 91·125   (e) 1728

8 This is the net of an open-topped box.

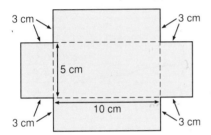

Calculate the volume of the box.

9 The base of the bottle
of orange is a circle
of diameter 7·5 cm.
The height of the
bottle is 30 cm. Anneka
is packaging it
in the smallest possible
box in the shape
of a cuboid.

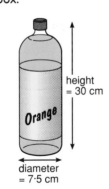

height
= 30 cm

diameter
= 7·5 cm

Calculate the lengths of the sides and
volume of that box.

10 The lengths of the three sides of a cuboid are 5 cm
by 4 cm by 8 cm.
Calculate:

(a) the volume of the cuboid
(b) the length of the sides of a cube which has a
volume equal to the volume of the cuboid.

A **wedge** can be constructed by slicing a cuboid
in half.

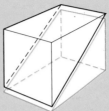

The volume of the wedge is then half the volume of
the cuboid.

11 For the wedges below, the lengths are all in
centimetres. Calculate the volume of each wedge.

(a)
5   6   4

(b)
10   12   6

(c)
5   12   10

(d)
8   10   15

(e)
9   30   20

(f)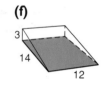
3   14   12

12

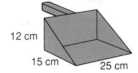

12 cm
15 cm   25 cm

Calculate the volume of the wedge-shaped part of
this scoop.

13 Calculate the volume of each of the solids below.

(a)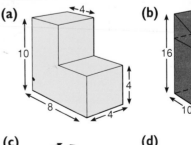
4   10   8   4

(b)
16   12   10   6

(c)
12   15   5   24

(d)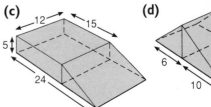
5   6   10   8

Around a circle

This circle has a radius of 4 cm.

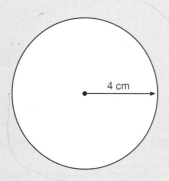

4 cm

The distance around the edge of the circle is called its **circumference**.

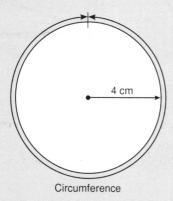

4 cm

Circumference

The **circumference of a circle radius 4 cm is approximately 25 cm**.

The formula for the circumference of a circle of radius r units is

$$C = 2 \times \pi \times r \quad \text{or} \quad C = 2\pi r$$

or, since the **diameter (d) of a circle is twice the radius**

$$C = \pi \times d \quad \text{or} \quad C = \pi d$$

You can calculate the circumference of a circle of radius 4 cm on a calculator.

Press [2] [×] [Π] [×] [4] [=] [25.13]

If your calculator does not have a [Π] button then you can use the approximation $\pi = 3 \cdot 14$

I Calculate the circumference of a circle of radius:

(a) 5 cm   (b) 8 cm   (c) 2·5 cm   (d) 10 cm

The circumference of a **semi-circle** is **half** the circumference of the circle.

2 Calculate the circumference of a semi-circle of radius:

(a) 4 cm   (b) 10 cm   (c) 12 cm   (d) 6·8 cm

3 A window is in the shape of a rectangle with a semi-circle.

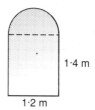

1·4 m

1·2 m

Calculate the total perimeter of the window.

4 A sheet of metal is in the shape of a rectangle with a semi-circle at each end.

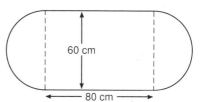

60 cm

80 cm

Calculate the total perimeter of the sheet of metal.

If we know the circumference of a circle we can calculate its radius using the formula

$$r = \frac{C}{2\pi} \quad \text{or} \quad \textbf{radius} = \textbf{Circumference} \div 2 \times \pi$$

and the diameter can be found either by
diameter = twice the radius
or using the formula

$$d = \frac{C}{\pi} \quad \text{or} \quad \textbf{diameter} = \textbf{Circumference} \div \pi$$

5 Calculate the radius of a circle with circumference:

(a) 10 cm   (b) 50 cm   (c) 27 cm   (d) 200 cm

6 Calculate the diameter of a circle of circumference:

(a) 60 cm   (b) 44 cm   (c) 314 cm   (d) 180·4 cm

This circle, of radius 4 units, has been drawn on squared paper.
The number of squares inside the circle has been counted or, for part squares, approximated.

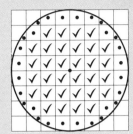

The circle contains the equivalent of about 50 squares.

The area of the circle is approximately 50 square units.

The formula to calculate exactly the area of a circle of radius r units is

Area = $\pi \times r \times r$ or   **$A = \pi r^2$**

Since the **diameter of a circle is twice the radius**, the formula to calculate the area of a circle, when we know its diameter, is

Area = $\dfrac{\pi \times d \times d}{4}$ or   **$A = \dfrac{\pi d^2}{4}$**

1 Calculate the area of a circle of radius:
   (a) 5 cm   **(b)** 4 cm   **(c)** 7 cm   **(d)** 10 cm.

2 Calculate the area of a circle of diameter:
   (a) 4 cm   **(b)** 10 cm   **(c)** 16 cm   **(d)** 3·2 cm.

The area of a **semi-circle** is **half** the area of the circle.

3 Calculate the area of:
   (a) a circle of radius 3·6 cm
   (b) a semi-circle of radius 18 cm
   (c) a circle of diameter 12 cm
   (d) a semi-circle of diameter 8·4 cm
   (e) a circle of diameter 5·6 cm
   (f) a circle of radius 7·6 cm.

4 This glass window is in the shape of a rectangle with a semi-circle.

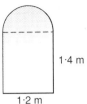

1·4 m

1·2 m

   (a) Calculate the area of the window.
   (b) The glass costs £26·50 per square metre. Calculate the cost of the glass in the window.

The radius or diameter of a circle can be found if we know the area. To do this we make use of the formulae

$r = \sqrt{\dfrac{A}{\pi}}$ and $d = \sqrt{\dfrac{4A}{\pi}}$

5 Calculate:
   (a) the radius of a circle of area:
   • 20 cm^2 • 314 cm^2 • 516·4 cm^2
   (b) the diameter of a circle of area:
   • 30 cm^2 • 142 cm^2 • 57·8 cm^2

6 Calculate:
   (a) the area of a circle of radius 7 cm
   (b) the length of the side of a square with the same area.

7 A rectangle measures 5 cm by 8 cm.
   Calculate:
   (a) the area of the rectangle
   (b) the radius of the circle which has an area equal to the area of the rectangle.

8 This rug is in the shape of a rectangle with two semi-circular ends.

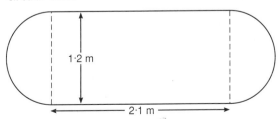

1·2 m

2·1 m

   (a) Calculate the area of the rug.
   (b) The cost of the rug is £75. Calculate the cost of the rug per square metre.

Albert's Autos

Albert keeps a **computer database** of the cars which are for sale in his yard.

A **database** is a collection of information.

Albert's computer database is shown in the print out.

Albert's Autos - Current Stock

Year	Registration	Make	Model	Colour	Miles	Price
1992	K	Rover	214Si	Red	7500	7995
1990	H	Austin	Maestro 1·3	Blue	21500	4750
1989	F	Ford	Sapphire 1·6	White	41000	3995
1983	Y	Vauxhall	Astra 1·3	Green	78000	995
1992	J	VW	Golf 1·8	Red	12000	8995
1990	H	BMW	320i	White	46000	8750
1986	D	Mazda	RX7	Black	67000	2950
1993	L	Vauxhall	Corsa 1·2	Blue	5000	7295
1992	K	Citroen	AX10	White	14000	5750
1993	K	Ford	Escort 1·8	Red	11000	7999
1989	F	Fiat	Panda 750L	Blue	52000	2695
1990	H	Nissan	Primera 1·6	Red	37000	5995
1993	K	Ford	Fiesta 1100LX	Red	9800	6495
1993	L	Peugeot	306XL	White	6000	9795
1991	J	Mazda	626	Black	30000	7995
1987	E	Austin	Montego	Red	63000	3995

1 How many cars are for sale in Albert's yard?

2 How many cars are:
   (a) red   **(b)** Vauxhall
   (c) K registration   **(d)** 1993 year
   (e) on sale for less than £5000?

3 **(a)** Which car is cheapest?
   (b) Which car costs most?
   (c) Which cars are black?
   (d) Which cars have recorded more than
        30 000 miles?
   (e) Which car is the oldest?

4 Mary wants to buy a red car costing less than £8000.
   List the cars Albert would show her.

5 Which car is blue and has done 5000 miles?

Albert would like to know if there is any
connection between **year** and **price**.
To see whether there is such a connection, he can
draw a **scatter graph**.
To do this he can:
• draw the axes for year and for price
• plot, for each car, the year against the price
• give the scatter graph a title.

This is the scatter graph of price against year.

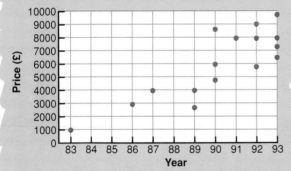

Albert's scatter graph shows that in general the
newer the car, the more it costs and the older the
car, the less it costs. There is no car that is very old
and costs a lot or very new and is cheap.
In general we can assume that the newer the car
the higher the cost.
This connection is called **correlation**. It shows
that there is a **relationship** between the year and
the price.

6 Draw a scatter graph to see if there is any
   correlation (connection) between year and miles.
   Remember to draw and label the axes.
   For each car, plot the year against the miles.
   Give the scatter graph a title.
   Comment on the correlation.

7 Draw a scatter graph to see if there is any
   correlation between miles and price.
   Remember to draw and label the axes.
   For each car, plot the miles against price.
   Give the scatter graph a title.
   Comment on the correlation.

You need a copy of a local newspaper.
The newspaper must contain some advertisements for
new and used cars.

8 Use your local newspaper to make a database on cars.
   Choose the information you wish to record.
   When you have completed the database:
   (a) Draw a scatter graph to see if there is any
        correlation between two of the features.
        Always remember to comment on the
        correlation.
   (b) Work in pairs.
        Exchange databases with your partner.
        Ask each other questions, such as:
        'Which cars are red?'
        'How many cars cost less than £7,500?'

9 Choose any idea of your own for which you could
   obtain information to make a database. Here are a
   few possibilities:
   • friends at school, their ages, gender, likes, dislikes,
      hair colour, part-time jobs
   • music, pop-groups, their records, their ages,
      number of hit records
   • sports teams, hockey, cricket, tennis, rugby, soccer,
      the colours of kits, places they play, numbers in a
      team, ages of players
   • newspapers, costs, sizes, number of readers, use of
      colour photographs, size of paper
   • countries, their populations, the climate,
      agriculture, industry, capital cities.

Whatever your choice, be sure to print accurate
information, make scatter graphs, draw conclusions and
present your information using appropriate statistical
diagrams.

Geoff plays football for Clarbury Town in the local league.

Teams can either Win, Draw or Lose a match. These are called the **outcomes** of a single match.

When Clarbury play two matches there are **9** different possible outcomes. Some of these outcomes are

- **Win   Win**
- **Draw   Win**
- **Lose   Lose**

1 Find the other 6 possible outcomes when Clarbury play two matches.

2 How many different possible outcomes will there be when Clarbury play 3 matches?

Geoff's sister, Lynn, plays tennis for Clarbury High School.

When she plays tennis she must either Win or Lose a match, these matches cannot end in a draw.

When she plays two matches the different possible outcomes are

- **Win   Win**
- **Win   Lose**
- **Lose   Win**
- **Lose   Lose**

and there are only **4** of them.

3 Write down all the different possible outcomes when Lynn plays:
(a) 3 matches   **(b)** 4 matches.

4 Copy and complete the table for the number of possible outcomes for Lynn playing tennis.

Number of matches	Number of possible outcomes
1	2
2	4
3	
4	
5	
n	

Some days Geoff plays football and Lynn plays tennis. There are several possible **joint outcomes**.

One possible joint outcome is
     Geoff Loses and **Lynn Wins**

another is
     Geoff Draws and **Lynn Loses.**

5 Write down all the possible joint outcomes when Geoff and Lynn play one match each.
(There are six of these joint outcomes.)

6 How many different possible joint outcomes are there when they play:
(a) 2 matches each   **(b)** 3 matches each?

Clarbury Town are awarded
3 points when they win, 1 point when they draw and **0 points when they lose**.

7 Calculate the number of points they will be awarded for the following outcomes:
(a) Win, Win, Draw   **(b)** Lose, Lose, Draw
(c) Draw, Draw, Lose   **(d)** Win, Lose, Draw.

8 Clarbury Town play 5 matches.
(a) Calculate the most number of points they can be awarded.
(b) Calculate the least number of points they can be awarded.
(c) Calculate any number of points between the least and most which they cannot be awarded.
(d) Write down a possible outcome for your answer to **(c)**.

Juliet and Martin Smith own a corner shop.
They always like their shop to look tidy.
When they stack tins they usually stack them in a
certain way to create a pattern.

One of their patterns is like this.

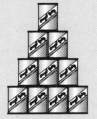

This is the **stage 4** pattern.
There are 10 tins.

This is the **stage 7** pattern.
There are 28 tins.

1 Draw the stage 5 and stage 6 patterns and count the number of tins in each.

2 Draw other stages of the pattern. Count and record the number of tins at each stage.

3 **Investigate** the number of tins in the pattern at various stages. Record your observations and results. Make and test any generalisations.

4 Suggest at least one other stacking arrangement that Juliet and Martin might consider. Investigate this arrangement.

Growing squares

You can develop a pattern starting with one red square.

This is **stage 1**.

Surround the single red square with blue squares.

This is **stage 2**.
You need 4 blue squares.

Surround this pattern with red squares.

This is **stage 3**.

Surround this pattern with blue squares.

This is **stage 4**.

You need squared paper.

1 Investigate how the pattern develops for different stages. In particular, examine the numbers of red and blue squares used at each stage.

2 Conduct a similar investigation but start with two squares.

Bob Ellis is planning a pathway, using paving stones.
His pathway is 6 metres long and 1 metre wide.
His paving stones are 1 metre long and $\frac{1}{2}$ metre wide.

One way of laying the stones is

another way is.

and a third way is

1 Show that for a path 3 metres long and 1 metre wide there are a total of 13 different ways of laying the 1 m by $\frac{1}{2}$ m paving slabs.

2 How many different ways would there be of laying the slabs if the pathway was 7 metres long by 1 metre wide? Explain your answer.

3 **Investigate** the number of different ways of laying the 1 m by $\frac{1}{2}$ m slabs for pathways which are 1 metre wide, but whose length could be any whole number of metres.

Illustrate your response with diagrams.
Make and record any observations and results.
Form and test any generalisations.
Explain your answers.

For her summer holiday Angela is going to visit two of her relatives for a week at each of their homes.

She has to choose two from a list of five relatives.

Aunt Joyce, Uncle Sam, Cousin Peter, Grandad Joe, Grandma Emily

One choice she could make is:
- Week 1 with Aunt Joyce and Week 2 with Grandma Emily

a different choice could be:
- Week 1 with Grandma Emily and Week 2 with Aunt Joyce

whilst a third choice could be:
- Week 1 with Cousin Peter and Week 2 with Grandad Joe.

1   List all the possible choices Angela could make. How many different choices does she have?

2   What happens if the list of relatives she could visit is extended from 5 to 6? How many different choices would she have then?

3   Change the number of relatives Angela could visit to any number of your own choice. Angela has to spend one week with each relative. **Investigate** the number of different choices Angela could make for these various numbers of relatives.

Record all your results or observations.
Try to make and test any general results.
Show all your working.
Write all of your explanations.

Beth and Henry Logan have a leaky bathroom pipe.
They ask a plumber to mend it.

They look in the local paper and see three advertisements
for plumbers who can do the job for them.

When they enquire about the costs, Beth and Henry
find that the charges are:

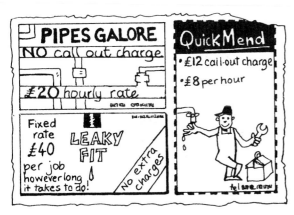

The job at Henry and Beth's house could take any length
of time to complete, from 1 hour to 6 hours.

1 Calculate the total charge which would be made by
each of the three plumbers for times of doing the job
that vary from 1 hour to 6 hours.

2 Use an appropriate method to record your results to
question 1.

3 The job at Henry and Beth's house takes the plumber
x hours to complete. Write a general expression,
involving x, for the total cost of doing the job.

4 Offer your advice to Henry and Beth as to which is
the cheapest plumber to use for specific times that it
might take to mend their pipe.

This grid has 7 spaces.

There are red frogs on three of the spaces and blue frogs on three of the other spaces.
The space in the middle of the grid has been left empty.
This is the **starting position**.

The aim of the game is to move the frogs so that the **finishing** position is

The frogs can only move in certain ways. They have to follow these rules:

Rule 1 A frog can slide into an empty space which is next to it.

Rule 2 A frog can jump over exactly one frog of the other colour to land
in an empty space.
So a red frog can jump over a blue frog and a blue frog can jump over a red frog.

Rule 3 The red frogs can only move to the right and the blue frogs can only move to the left.

1 Show that with the original six frogs, three red and three blue, it is possible to get
from the starting position to the finishing position in a minimum of 15 moves.

2 Investigate the minimum number of moves required to complete the game for
different numbers of red and blue frogs.

Alter the number of red and blue frogs and the size of the grid.
Keep the number of red frogs equal to the number of blue frogs.
Keep the size of the grid always one more than the total number of frogs.
Always start the game with the red frogs on the left, the blue on the right and the
centre space empty.
The game always finishes when all the red and blue frogs have exchanged positions.

This square 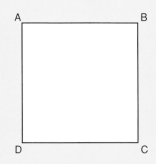 has **4 lines of symmetry**.

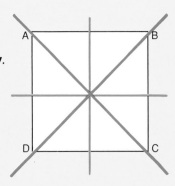

The square also has **4 rotational symmetries** through angles of 90°, 180°, 270° and 360° (or 0°) as shown below.

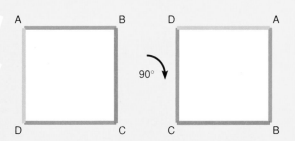

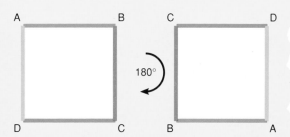

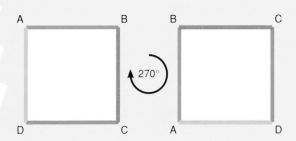

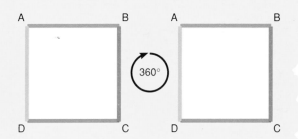

A square has a total of **8 symmetries**.

1 Find, giving your explanation in each case, the number of symmetries of each of these shapes:

(a) a rectangle

(b) an equilateral triangle

(c) an isosceles triangle

(d) a Union Jack flag

(e) a twenty pence coin

(f) a circle.

A square is **a regular polygon with 4 sides**.

2 Investigate the relationship between the number of sides of a regular polygon and its total number of symmetries.

Illustrate your response with appropriate diagrams.
Set out your results clearly.
Record any observations or comments.
Make, test or justify any general statements.

Divide (and multiply) and rule

1 (a) Mark has been given this number pattern.
Copy and complete it.

$5 \times 2 = 10$
$4 \times 2 = 8$
$3 \times 2 = 6$
$2 \times 2 = 4$
$1 \times 2 = 2$
$0 \times 2 = 0$
$^-1 \times 2 = \square$
$^-2 \times 2 = \square$
$^-3 \times 2 = \square$
$^-4 \times 2 = \square$

(b) Check your answers with those of a friend to
see if you agree.

2 Use your answers to question **1** to help you find the
answers to:

(a) $^-5 \times 2$ **(b)** $^-7 \times 2$ **(c)** $^-10 \times 2$
(d) $^-4 \times 3$ **(e)** $^-3 \times 5$ **(f)** $^-1 \times 12$

3 Copy and complete this number pattern:

$3 \times ^-5 = ^-15$
$3 \times ^-4 = ^-12$
$3 \times ^-3 = \square$
$3 \times ^-2 = \square$
$3 \times ^-1 = \square$
$3 \times 0 = \square$
$3 \times 1 = \square$

4 What is:

(a) $3 \times ^-6$ **(b)** $3 \times ^-10$ **(c)** $3 \times ^-12$
(d) $4 \times ^-3$ **(e)** $3 \times ^-5$ **(f)** $1 \times ^-12$?

5 Copy and complete this number pattern:

$^-4 \times 4 = ^-16$
$^-4 \times 3 = ^-12$
$^-4 \times 2 = \square$
$^-4 \times 1 = \square$
$^-4 \times 0 = 0$
$^-4 \times ^-1 = \square$
$^-4 \times ^-2 = \square$
$^-4 \times ^-3 = \square$
$^-4 \times ^-4 = 16$

6 What is:

(a) $^-4 \times ^-5$ **(b)** $^-4 \times ^-8$ **(c)** $^-4 \times ^-10$
(d) $^-2 \times ^-2$ **(e)** $^-5 \times ^-3$ **(f)** $^-3 \times ^-3$
(g) $^-6 \times ^-1$ **(h)** $^-7 \times ^-2$ **(i)** $^-8 \times ^-0.5$?

Rules for multiplication

- $(+) \times (+) = (+)$
- $(+) \times (-) = (-)$
- $(-) \times (+) = (-)$
- $(-) \times (-) = (+)$

7 Find:

(a) $3 \times ^-4$ **(b)** $6 \times ^-6$ **(c)** $^-1 \times ^-1$
(d) $^-5 \times ^-2$ **(e)** 4×8 **(f)** $8 \times ^-5$
(g) $^-8 \times 0$ **(h)** $^-2 \times ^-8$ **(i)** $^-9 \times 3$

8 Find:

(a) $(^-3 \times 5) \times ^-2$ **(b)** $(^-2 \times ^-4) \times 3$
(c) $(^-2 \times ^-2) \times ^-2$ **(d)** $(3 \times ^-1) \times 6$
(e) $^-2 \times (^-2 \times ^-2)$ **(f)** $3 \times (^-1 \times 6)$
(g) $^-2 \times ^-3 \times 4$ **(h)** $^-2 \times 5 \times ^-3$
(i) $^-4 \times 5 \times ^-5$ **(j)** $6 \times ^-2 \times ^-6$

Rules for division

- $(+) \div (+) = (+)$
- $(+) \div (-) = (-)$
- $(-) \div (+) = (-)$
- $(-) \div (-) = (+)$

9 Find:

(a) $^-6 \div ^-3$ **(b)** $8 \div ^-2$ **(c)** $^-14 \div ^-7$
(d) $20 \div ^-5$ **(e)** $^-24 \div 6$ **(f)** $18 \div 3$
(g) $^-45 \div ^-5$ **(h)** $32 \div ^-8$ **(i)** $16 \div ^-4$

10 Find:

(a) $(8 + ^-2) \times ^-3$ **(b)** $(^-4 + ^-5) \times 2$
(c) $(8 - ^-2) \times ^-6$ **(d)** $(^-6 - ^-4) \times 5$
(e) $(17 + ^-2) \div ^-3$ **(f)** $(12 - ^-12) \div 24$
(g) $(25 - 16) \times 4$

11 Find:

(a) $\dfrac{8 \times 2}{4}$ **(b)** $\dfrac{^-4 \times ^-5}{^-2}$

(c) $\dfrac{^-6 \times 6}{12}$ **(d)** $\dfrac{8 \times ^-5}{^-4}$

(e) $\dfrac{^-6 \times ^-8}{^-3 \times 4}$ **(f)** $\dfrac{^-10 \times 6}{^-3 \times ^-5}$

(g) $(^-2)^2$ **(h)** $(^-3)^2$ **(i)** $(^-2)^3$

1 Round each of these numbers to the nearest 10

   (a) 278   **(b)** 139   **(c)** 64   **(d)** 66

   (e) 13   **(f)** 555   **(g)** 199   **(h)** 342

   (i) 8   **(j)** 603   **(k)** 719   **(l)** 4

2 Round each of these to the nearest whole number.

   (a) 4·9   **(b)** 7·2   **(c)** 56·8   **(d)** 45·1

   (e) 0·67   **(f)** 15·9   **(g)** 78·2   **(h)** 19·9

   (i) 8·2   **(j)** 80·3   **(k)** 0·2   **(l)** 3·06

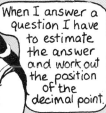

Natalie's calculator has developed a fault. It does not indicate the decimal point

When I answer a question I have to estimate the answer and work out the position of the decimal point.

When working out the answer to 2·1 × 3·9, her calculator read

2·1 is approximately 2 and
3·9 is approximately 4
Since 2 × 4 = 8
2·1 × 3·9 must be 8·12

3 Rewrite each of these questions with each number written to the nearest whole number.

   (a) 2·2 × 4·9

   (b) 4·8 × 5·2

   (c) 6·4 × 2·9

   (d) 12·3 × 1·8

   (e) 3·2 × 2·9

4 Work out the answers to the questions you wrote in question **3**.

5 These are some questions and their answer given by Natalie's calculator. Copy each question and answer, putting in the decimal point.

   (a) 3·8 × 4·2 = 1 5 9 6

   (b) 3·1 × 1·8 = 5 5 8

   (c) 7·8 × 8·3 = 6 4 7 4

   (d) 5·1 × 9·9 = 5 0 5 9

   (e) 12·3 × 11·8 = 1 4 5 1 4

   (f) 25·2 ÷ 4·9 = 5 1 4 2 8

   (g) 102·9 ÷ 9·9 = 1 0 3 9 3 9

THE FRIENDSHIP & OTHER STORIES
MILDRED D TAYLOR

£1·99

Errol has been asked to find the approximate cost of 12 books costing £1·99 each. £1·99 is almost £2 so an approximate cost would be 12 × £2 = £24

6 Find the approximate cost of:

   (a) 9 books costing £1·99 each

   (b) 10 packets of sweets costing 95p each

   (c) 6 screwdrivers costing £4·05 each

   (d) 4 radios costing £29·90 each

   (e) 120 razor blades costing 52p each.

Natalie may have a broken calculator but I haven't got a calculator at all!

Jaswinder has to estimate all his answers to the nearest whole number.

Given the question 62 ÷ 11
Jaswinder works out
62 is approximately 60
11 is approximately 10
So an estimate for the answer is 60 ÷ 10 = 6

In this example it would have been equally good to estimate the answer as 60 ÷ 12 = 5

7 Estimate the answer to these questions giving your answer as a whole number.

   (a) 37 ÷ 5   **(b)** 46 ÷ 8   **(c)** 104 ÷ 11

   (d) 147 ÷ 49   **(e)** 238 ÷ 29   **(f)** 198 ÷ 18

   (g) 278 ÷ 39   **(h)** 690 ÷ 102   **(i)** 350 ÷ 58

8 Estimate an approximate answer to:

   (a) $\dfrac{52 \times 2}{11}$ **(b)** $\dfrac{37 \times 5}{21}$ **(c)** $\dfrac{24 \times 11}{59}$

   (d) $\dfrac{13 \times 58}{5}$ **(e)** $\dfrac{19 \times 21}{79}$ **(f)** $\dfrac{52 \times 1·9}{4}$

   (g) $\dfrac{242}{16 \times 4}$ **(h)** $\dfrac{550}{9 \times 13}$ **(i)** $\dfrac{31 \times 19}{9 \times 21}$

Some things are more equal

In a bottle of Pepsy two secret ingredients are added in the ratio 5:7. If there is 4·5 ml of the first ingredient, how much of the second ingredient must be added?

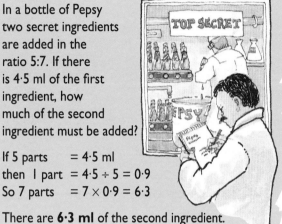

If 5 parts   = 4·5 ml
then 1 part = 4·5 ÷ 5 = 0·9
So 7 parts   = 7 × 0·9 = 6·3

There are **6·3 ml** of the second ingredient.

1 Over Easter, Jim, Jack and Kate eat their way through a large number of mini Easter eggs in the ratio 3:4:5. Jim eats 27 eggs on his own.
   (a) If 3 parts equal 27, what is the value of 1 part?
   (b) How many eggs did Kate eat?
   (c) How many eggs did they eat altogether?

2 Mr and Mrs Kildare both have their own cars. The ratio of the fuel consumption is 4:3.
   Mr Kildare's car has a fuel consumption of 10 km per litre of petrol. How many km per litre does Mrs Kildare's car do?

3 These two towers are similar. The base of the first tower is 6 m and the second 8 m.
   (a) What is the ratio of the two towers in its lowest form?
   (b) Calculate the height of the second tower.

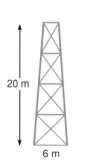

20 m

6 m   8 m

4 Calculate the height of the second triangle.

 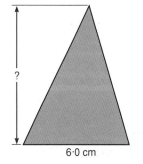

3 cm

?

2·4 cm   6·0 cm

5 In French towns the speed limit is 60 km/h. If 5 miles is approximately equal to 8 km:

RAPPEL

   (a) write as a ratio the distance in miles to the distance in kilometres
   (b) write the ratio in the form 1:n
   (c) find the speed limit in French towns in miles per hour
   (d) find the metric equivalent to 70 mph.

6 Flour and yeast are mixed in the ratio 20:1 in order to make bread.
   (a) In a total mix of 5·46 kg, how much of the mixture is flour?
   (b) How much yeast is needed to mix with 420 g of flour?

7 The ratio of the examination marks of three students was 4:5:7. If the middle mark of the three students was 45% what was:
   (a) the highest mark
   (b) the difference between the lowest and the highest marks?

8 This graph shows the height of a tree and the length of the shadow it casts.
   (a) Write the ratio of the length of the shadow to the height of the tree.
   (b) Find the height of a tree which casts a shadow 8 m long.
   (c) Find the length of the shadow cast by a tree 20 m tall.
   (d) The length of the shadow and the height of the tree add up to 59·5 m, how high is the tree?

15

Height of tree (m)

10

5

0   1   2   3   4   5   6
Length of shadow (m)

In 1994 a packet of biscuits cost 60p. In 1995 a similar packet cost 72p. What was the percentage increase?

actual increase 72 − 60 = 12p

$$\text{fraction increase} = \frac{\text{actual increase}}{\text{original price}} = \frac{12}{60}$$

$\frac{12}{60}$ as a decimal fraction = 0·2

Percentage increase = 0·2 × 100 = 20%

1 In 1996 a similar packet of biscuits had increased to 80p. Find:
   (a) the fractional increase • from 1994 • from 1995
   (b) the percentage increase • from 1994 • from 1995.

2 Calculate the percentage increase from:
   (a) £24 to £33
   (b) 12·5 kg to 20 kg
   (c) 2·45 m to 2·86 m
   (d) 50 seconds to 1 minute.

3 Before fitting a 'fuel-saver', Jamie's car travelled 36 km on 4·5 litres of petrol. After fitting the fuel-saver, it travelled 58·3 km on 5·5 litres. Find:
   (a) the fuel consumption (km/litre) before the fuel saver was fitted
   (b) the fuel consumption (km/litre) after it was fitted
   (c) the percentage change in fuel consumption.

4

Arthur Weekly buys an old cottage for £64 000. He spends £8400 on repairs and renovation. He then puts the cottage up for sale. Find:
   (a) his actual profit
   (b) his percentage profit, to the nearest 1%

2 Bedroomed Character cottage FOR SALE £125,000 FULLY RENOVATED

5 A mechanic at a garage drew 0·75 litres of oil from a 21-litre oil drum, which was exactly $\frac{1}{3}$ full. Find the percentage of the original amount that was left in the drum.

Liz invests £800 in a company, Down Hills Ltd. One year later, she finds her investment is only worth £680. To find her percentage loss, first find the actual loss

actual loss = £800 − £680 = £120

fractional loss = $\frac{120}{800}$

$\frac{120}{800}$ as a decimal fraction = 0·15

Percentage loss = 0·15 × 100 = 15%

6 One year later Liz's investment had fallen to £590. Find:
   (a) her actual loss over the two years
   (b) her percentage loss over the two years
   (c) her percentage loss between the second and third years.

7 Find the percentage decrease, to the nearest 1%, from:
   (a) £45 to £36
   (b) 5·2 kg to 3·8 kg
   (c) 45 cm to 39·5 cm
   (d) 2 min to 110 seconds
   (e) 1 metre to 45 cm

8 This table shows the value of the Rondel car after a number of years, from new.

Price	£
new	12 500
after 1 year	10 000
after 2 years	8 600
after 3 years	7 500
after 4 years	6 600

   (a) Calculate the percentage loss for each year as a percentage of the original price.
   (b) Calculate the percentage loss between the second and third years.
   (c) Between which two years was there the smallest percentage loss?

9 Jason bought a house in 1986 for £64 000.
   In 1990 he sold it to Sanjit for £78 000.
   In 1994 Sanjit had to sell the house for £69 000.
   Calculate:
   (a) Jason's percentage profit
   (b) Sanjit's percentage loss
   (c) the percentage change in the value of the house between 1986 and 1994.

Growing up

Toni has been given this problem to solve. What multiplier must be applied to change the smaller square into the larger one?

14 cm²

5 cm² → × ? →

To find the multiplier, calculate the value of:

$$\frac{\text{the area of the larger square}}{\text{the area of the smaller square}} = \frac{14}{5} = 2.8$$

The multiplier is 2·8, or the larger square is 2·8 times bigger than the smaller square.

1 Calculate the value of the multiplier in each of these.

(a)

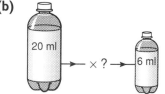
4 kg → × ? → 9 kg

(b)

20 ml → × ? → 6 ml

(c)

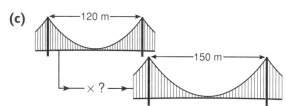
←120 m→
←150 m→
→ × ? →

2 (a) Measure the width of this photograph.

(b) The photograph is to be enlarged by Prontopix so that the new width is 7 cm. What 'multiplier' must be applied?

(c) Calculate the new length of the photograph.

3 Prontopix are reducing this photograph to fit into a magazine. The length required is 4·8 cm.

length

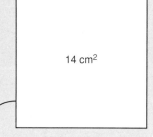

height

(a) Measure the length of the photograph.
(b) Calculate the multiplier.
(c) Calculate the new height.

4 If two similar shapes have a ratio of 2:3, what is the multiplier of:
(a) the smaller shape to the larger one
(b) the larger shape to the smaller one?

5 Two similar towers are in the ratio 2:3. If the smaller tower is 17 m high, how high is the taller tower?

6 An engineer makes a model car which is 12 cm long. He wants to make a second model to put on display. The ratio of the smaller model to the larger one is 3:7. Find the length of the second model.

7 Calculate the new length and width of this design, correct to 1 dp, if it is to be enlarged in the ratio:
(a) 4:5
(b) 3:10
(c) 2·4 : 3·2
(d) 6:5
(e) 7:2

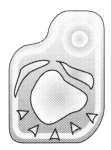

8 This pirate's treasure map has to be enlarged in the ratio 7:12. What distance on the new map will represent the same as 4 cm on the old one?

Map scales can be written in two different ways:

- as a ratio. A ratio of 1 : 500 000 means any distance on the map is 500 000 times bigger on the ground.
- as a scale. 1 cm = 5 km. This means that 1 cm on the map is 5 km on the ground.

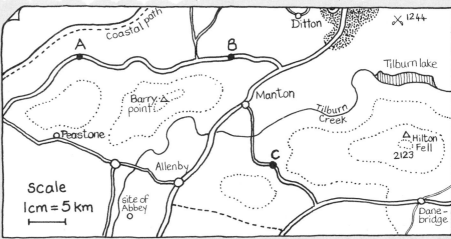

In this example, the ratio 1 : 500 000 and the scale 1 cm = 5 km represent the same thing. However, it is not usual to put both systems on one map.

On the map the distance A to B is 4 cm. This means the actual distance is
- 4 × 500 000 = 2 000 000 cm = 20 km or
- 4 × 5 = 20 km

---

1 **(a)** Measure the distance A to C on the map above.
  (b) What is the actual distance in:
   - cm   • km?

2 This is part of a map showing the south-west corner of England. The scale of the map is 1 cm = 10 km.

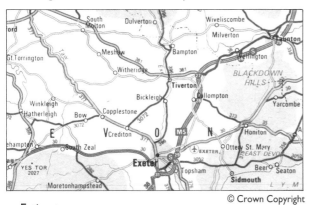

© Crown Copyright

Estimate:
(a) the distance between Exeter and South Molton on the map, in centimetres
(b) the actual distance from Exeter to South Molton, in kilometres.

3 A map is drawn to a ratio of 1 : 150 000
  (a) What is the actual distance in km of a distance on the map of 4·5 cm?
  (b) What distance on the map represents a true distance of 22·5 km?

4 The scale of a map is 1 cm = 20 km
  (a) What is this scale written as a ratio?
  (b) What distance on the map represents:
   - 48 km   • 62·5 km?

5 The actual distance in a straight line, between Buckholm and Lauder is 10 km. Find:
  (a) the scale in the form 1 cm = x km
  (b) the ratio of the map scale to the actual distance.

© Crown Copyright

Simple equations 2

Alan has been asked to write this problem in maths shorthand.

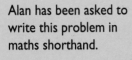

Three times a number, add 5 is the same as twice the number, take-away 1.

let n be the number

Alan starts by saying
Let n be the number

Three times a number add 5 $3n + 5$

Twice the number take away 1 $2n - 1$

'is the same as' means $3n + 5 = 2n - 1$

Solving the equation $3n + 2 = n + 8$
This time there are n's on both sides of the equation.
However:

$3n + 2 = n + 8$ means $n + n + n + 2 = n + 8$

Cancelling an n from both sides,
the equation becomes $n + n + 2 = 8$

or $2n + 2 = 8$

which means $\boxed{6} + 2 = 8$

or $2n = 6$

$n = 3$

---

1 Write each of these in maths shorthand:

(a) Three times a number add 2, is the same as the number add 3

(b) Multiplying a number by 4 and then taking away 5, gives the same result as multiplying the number by 7 and adding 3

(c) Two times the number add 1 equals the number minus 4

(d) If you take a certain number away from 10, you get the same result as multiplying it by 4 and adding 6.

(e) A number add 4 is then multiplied by 3. This gives the same answer as multiplying the number by 5 and subtracting 2.

2 Explain to your teacher or to a friend the meaning of these equations:

(a) $4n + 5 = 3n - 2$

(b) $2n - 3 = 4n - 5$

(c) $6n + 2 = 3n - 12$

(d) $3(n + 1) = 2n + 5$

(e) $2n - 6 = 5(n + 3)$

(f) $2(3n + 4) = 3(n - 1)$

3 What does the equation $3n + 2 = n + 8$ tell us about the distance between A and B?

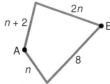

4 By cancelling n's on a one-for-one-basis from both sides of these equations, rewrite them so that the n appears on only one side.

(a) $3n + 2 = n - 4$ (b) $3n + 4 = 2n + 5$

(c) $5n - 3 = 2n + 6$ (d) $3n + 6 = 5n - 3$

(e) $4n + 5 = 5n - 3$ (f) $5n - 3 = 4n$

5 Try to work out how to have n's on one side of the equation only when:

(a) $2n + 3 = 4 - n$ (b) $3n + 5 = 4 - 2n$

6 Solve these equations:

(a) $3n + 2 = n + 6$ (b) $4n + 5 = 3n + 10$

(c) $5n - 5 = 2n + 7$ (d) $2n + 3 = 3n - 3$

(e) $2n - 4 = 5n + 2$ (f) $2n + 7 = 16 - n$

(g) $12 - 2n = 6 + 2n$ (h) $10n - 11 = 4n + 7$

(i) $7n - 8 = 19 - 2n$ (j) $3n + 2 = 18 - 5n$

(k) $6n - 2 = 4n - 12$ (l) $9n + 5 = 3n - 19$

7 Solve these equations by first expanding the bracket.

(a) $5(n + 1) = 15$

(b) $7(n - 3) = 14$

(c) $3(n - 4) = 2n$

(d) $2(2n + 4) = 5n$

(e) $3(2n + 4) = 2n + 2$

(f) $3(n + 4) = 2(n - 4)$

(g) $4(2n - 5) = 2(3n + 7)$

(h) $4(n + 1) = 2(n - 3) + 20$

(i) $3(n + 1) = 5(n + 2) - 1$

(j) $4(2n - 5) = 21 - 3(3n + 8)$

Beverley has been asked to translate this sentence into a mathematical statement.

I think of a number, square it, then subtract 12, to get an answer of 24.

Let n be the number n

Square the number n^2

Subtract 12 $n^2 - 12$

The answer is $n^2 - 12 = 24$

1 Translate these sentences into mathematical statements:

(a) a number is squared and 5 added to get an answer of 29

(b) 15 is taken away from a number that has been squared. This leaves a result of 52

(c) 61 is obtained if a number is squared, and 7 added

(d) a number that has been squared is taken away from 12 to leave minus 5

(e) five is added to a number, and the result squared. This gives an answer of 21

(f) a number is squared and added to 5 times the number. From this result, 6 is subtracted, to leave an answer of 100.

Find the number n, correct to 2 decimal places, if $n^2 + 6 = 38$

Start by writing 'something add 6 equals 38' $\boxed{?} + 6 = 38$

The something must be $\boxed{32} + 6 = 38$

This means that $n^2 = 32$
and so $n = \sqrt{32}$
   $n = 5.66$ to 2 dp

2 Find, correct to 2 decimal places the value of n if:

(a) $n^2 + 5 = 24$ **(b)** $n^2 - 11 = 50$
(c) $n^2 - 12 = 100$ **(d)** $25 + n^2 = 70$
(e) $28 - n^2 = 10$ **(f)** $n^2 + 12.5 = 22.5$
(g) $n^2 - 15 = 72.5$ **(h)** $n^2 - 10.2 = 68.4$
(i) $15 - n^2 = 14.5$ **(j)** $24.5 + n^2 = 36.5$

Solve the equation $2n^2 + 15 = 75$

Start by writing 'something add 15 equals 75' $\boxed{?} + 15 = 75$

This something must be $\boxed{60} + 15 = 75$

This means that $2n^2 = 60$

and so $n^2 = 30$

   $n = 5.48$ to 2 dp

3 Solve these equations:

(a) $2n^2 = 72$ **(b)** $3n^2 = 27$
(c) $2n^2 + 6 = 106$ **(d)** $3n^2 - 4 = 143$
(e) $4n^2 - 7 = 29$ **(f)** $5n^2 + 8 = 120$
(g) $52 - 2n^2 = 12$ **(h)** $12 + 5n^2 = 217$
(i) $2n^2 + 4 = 20.5$ **(j)** $4n^2 - 7 = 86.4$

4 Find the value of n:

(a)

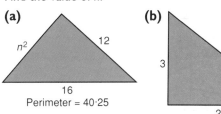

n^2 12
16
Perimeter = 40.25

(b)

3   5
$2n^2$
Perimeter = 12 cm

(c)

n
Area = 84.5 cm^2 $2n$

(d)

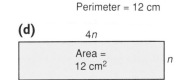

$4n$
Area = 12 cm^2 n

The plot thickens

This is a mapping diagram of
$x \longrightarrow 2x - 1$

input		output
4	$\longrightarrow$	7
3	$\longrightarrow$	5
2	$\longrightarrow$	3
1	$\longrightarrow$	1
0	$\longrightarrow$	‾1

The inputs and outputs can be linked together as a pair of coordinates

$(0, ‾1), (1, 1), (2, 3), (3, 5),$ and $(4, 7)$

These coordinates can then be plotted on to a coordinate diagram to give a graph of
$x \longrightarrow 2x - 1$ or a graph of $y = 2x - 1$

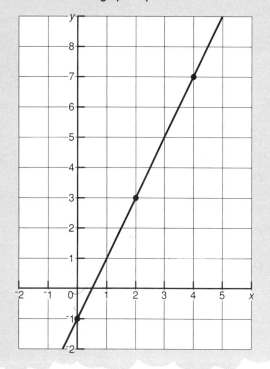

1

3	$\longrightarrow$	11
2	$\longrightarrow$	8
1	$\longrightarrow$	5
0	$\longrightarrow$	2
‾1	$\longrightarrow$	‾1

4	$\longrightarrow$	2
2	$\longrightarrow$	4
0	$\longrightarrow$	6
‾2	$\longrightarrow$	8
‾4	$\longrightarrow$	10

(a) Write the input and output of each diagram as sets of coordinates.

(b) Find the rule of each mapping diagram expressed in the form $x \longrightarrow$?

(c) On a suitable coordinate diagram, plot the points and join them up with a straight line.

(d) Write the name of each graph in the form $y =$?

2 For each of the following, draw a mapping diagram, write the set of coordinates and draw the graph.

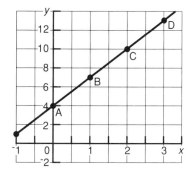

input

(a) $x \longrightarrow 3x - 2$ $(‾1, 0, 1, 2, 3)$
(b) $x \longrightarrow x + 2$ $(‾1, 0, 1, 2, 3)$
(c) $x \longrightarrow 3 + 2x$ $(‾1, 0, 1, 2, 3, 4,)$
(d) $x \longrightarrow 6 - x$ $(‾2, ‾1, 0, 1, 2)$
(e) $x \longrightarrow ‾2x - 3$ $(‾2, ‾1, 0, 1, 2, 3)$

3 This graph has been drawn from a certain mapping diagram.

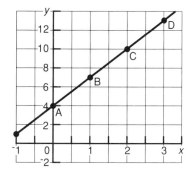

(a) Write the coordinates of points A, B, C and D.

(b) Use these coordinate points to draw a mapping diagram.

(c) Use the mapping diagram to work out the relationship in the form $y =$?

4 (a) For both these graphs select at least 4 sets of coordinate points to draw a corresponding mapping diagram.

(b) Find the relationship between input and output in the form $x \longrightarrow$? and $y =$?

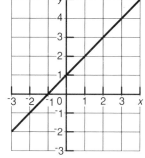
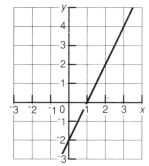

5 Work out the relationships represented by these graphs in the form:

(a) $x \longrightarrow$? **(b)** $y = $?

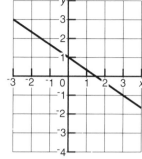

6 This mapping diagram is for the relationship

$x \longrightarrow x^2$

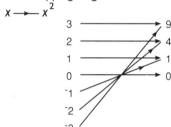

(a) Write the 7 coordinate pairs shown.
(b) Copy this diagram and plot the 7 points.
(c) Join the points with a **smooth curve.**

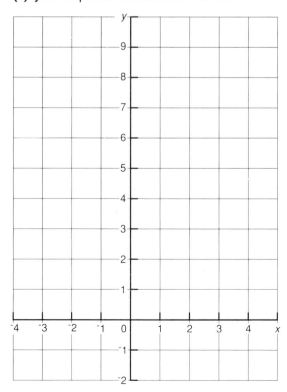

7 (a) Make a second copy of the diagram used in question **6**.
(b) Draw a mapping diagram for $x \longrightarrow x^2 + 1$ for input values of $^-3$ to 3
(c) Write 7 coordinate points using the input and output values of your mapping diagram.
(d) Plot the points and join them with a smooth curve.

8 Use the two graphs you have drawn for questions **6** and **7** to draw a graph of $y = x^2 - 1$ for values of x of $^-3$ to 3

9 This is a mapping diagram for $x \longrightarrow 4 - x^2$

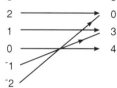

(a) Write the input and output as coordinate pairs.
(b) Copy this coordinate diagram.

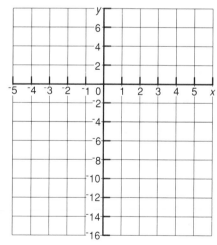

(c) Plot the points and join them with a smooth curve.
(d) Extend your curve as far as $x = ^-4$
(e) Find the value of y when $x = ^-4$

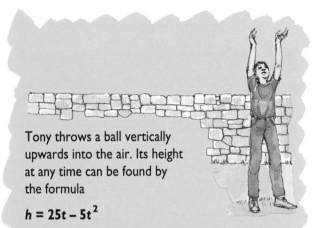

Tony throws a ball vertically
upwards into the air. Its height
at any time can be found by
the formula

$$h = 25t - 5t^2$$

where h is the height in metres above the point
from which it was thrown and
t is the time in seconds since the ball
was thrown.

1 **(a)** Using the input of $t = 0$ to 5, work out 6 pairs of
coordinate points.

(b) On graph paper make a
copy of this coordinate
diagram.
Plot the points and join
them with a smooth
curve.

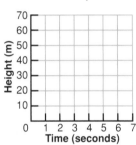

(c) Use your graph to find the height of the ball after
1·5 seconds.

(d) At what times was the ball at a height of
20 metres?

(e) What was the maximum height reached by
the ball?

(f) How long did it take to reach its maximum height?

2 Gaynor throws a second ball vertically into the air.
The height of this ball at any time after it was thrown
can be found using the formula

$$h = 35t - 5t^2$$

(a) Using an input of $t = 0$ to 7, work out the
corresponding coordinate points.

(b) On the same graph as in question 1, plot the
points and join them.

(c) If both balls were thrown at the same time
whose was first to reach its maximum height?

(d) How long after Tony's ball reached the ground
did Gaynor's ball reach the ground?

3 Ken's house has a rectangular garden, surrounded by
walls. He has 10 metres of wire netting. He uses the
netting to make a rectangular pen in which to keep
his pet rabbits.

(a) If one length of the netting is 6 metres, find:
• the length of the other side
• the area enclosed by the netting and the walls.

(b) Copy and complete the table showing the
lengths of one side from 0 up to 10 metres.

Length of one side	Width of the other side	Area enclosed
0	10	
1		
2		
9		
10		

(c) Draw a graph of area against length, to show the
information in your table.

(d) What is the length of the netting when the area
is 15 m²?

On trial

Algebra:
Solving quadratic
equations by trial
and improvement

106

Lisa has to solve this equation
$$x^2 = 12$$
by using a trial and improvement method.
If $x^2 = 12$ then $x = \sqrt{12}$.

Start by finding the two
whole numbers between $3^2 = 9$
which the square root of $4^2 = 16$
12 must be.

x must be between 3 and 4

Try 3·5	$3·5 \times 3·5 = 12·25$	too big
Try 3·4	$3·4 \times 3·4 = 11·56$	too small
Try 3·45	$3·45 \times 3·45 = 11·90$	too small
Try 3·46	$3·46 \times 3·46 = 11·97$	too small
Try 3·47	$3·47 \times 3·47 = 12·04$	too big

The answer must lie between $x = 3·46$ and $x = 3·47$

Try 3·465
$3·465 \times 3·465 = 12·006 = 12·01$ to 2 dp

Try 3·464
$3·464 \times 3·464 = 11·9992 = 12·00$ to 2 dp

If $x^2 = 12$ then $x = 3·464$

1 For each of these equations write the two whole
numbers between which the value of x must be:

(a) $x^2 = 20$ (b) $x^2 = 70$ (c) $x^2 = 120$
(d) $x^2 = 45$ (e) $x^2 = 2$ (f) $x^2 = 0·5$

2 Solve these equations, using a trial and improvement
method. Give your answers correct to 2 dp.

(a) $x^2 = 7$ (b) $x^2 = 27$ (c) $x^2 = 90$
(d) $x^2 = 110$ (e) $x^2 = 1·56$ (f) $x^2 = 0·68$

3 Using a trial and improvement method, find the
length of each side of these shapes.

(a)
x

| Area = 20·5 cm² |
x

(b)
$2x$

| Area = 65 cm² |
x

Colin has been asked to find the solution to this
equation
$$x^2 + 3x = 64$$
correct to one decimal place.

He has been told the solution is between
$x = 6$ and $x = 7$

When $x = 6$ $x^2 + 3x = 6^2 + 3 \times 6 = 54$
When $x = 7$ $x^2 + 3x = 7^2 + 3 \times 7 = 70$

Try $x = 6·5$ $6·5^2 + 3 \times 6·5 = 61·75$
Try $x = 6·6$ $6·6^2 + 3 \times 6·6 = 63·36$
Try $x = 6·7$ $6·7^2 + 3 \times 6·7 = 64·99$

The solution is between $x = 6·6$ and $x = 6·7$

Try $x = 6·65$ $6·65^2 + 3 \times 6·65 = 64·1725$
Try $x = 6·64$ $6·64^2 + 3 \times 6·64 = 64·0096$

$64·0096 = 64·0$ correct to 1 dp

So **$x = 6·64$** is the solution correct to 1 dp

4 Solve each of these equations correct to 1 decimal place:
(a) $x^2 + 5x = 43$ start with $x = 5$
(b) $x^2 + 2x = 70$ start with $x = 7$
(c) $x^2 - 2x = 85$ start with $x = 10$
(d) $x^2 - 5x = 7$ start with $x = 6$
(e) $x^2 + 3x = 5$ start with $x = 1$
(f) $x^2 + 2x = 200$ start with $x = 13$

5 (a) Copy and complete this table.

x	$x^2 + 5x$
1	6
2	14
3	24
4	
5	
6	
7	
8	

(b) Solve these equations, correct to 2 decimal places:
- $x^2 + 5x = 10$ • $x^2 + 5x = 80$
- $x^2 + 5x = 0$

The year after their holiday in Ireland, Gulzar and her family decide to go on a tour of Scotland.

Gulzar has learnt about **bearings**.

These are the four main compass points north, south, east and west.

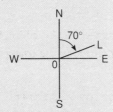

The north-south and east-west lines meet at O.
The **bearing of L from O**, or
the **bearing of the line OL**
is **070°**, because the angle $\widehat{NOL} = 70°$

To work out a **bearing** of a point P from O,
Gulzar knows that she must find the **clockwise angle from ON to OP**.
Bearings are always written as three figure numbers.

Here are three different bearings.

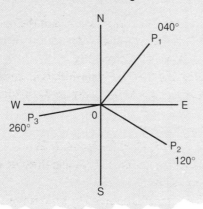

You need a protractor.

1 Measure and record, as three figure numbers, these bearings.

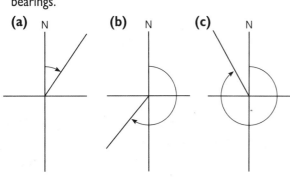

2 Draw a diagram, showing bearings of:
   (a) 030°   (b) 130°   (c) 250°   (d) 320°

3 Gulzar uses this map to help with her journey.

SCALE
1cm = 64km

Give the bearing of:
(a) Dundee from Glasgow
(b) Ben Hope from Glasgow
(c) Aberdeen from Inverness
(d) Thurso from Aberdeen
(e) Montrose from Aberdeen
(f) Kilmarnock from Montrose.
Write all your answers correct to the nearest degree.

4 One day Gulzar and her family plan to set out from their campsite, C, and travel 5 km due north to a landmark, L. At L they plan to turn onto a bearing of 060° and travel a further 10 km to a hotel, H.
They then plan to travel in a straight line back to C.
   (a) Make a scale diagram showing their proposed journey, using a scale of 1 cm to represent 1 km.
   (b) Find the bearing of H from C.

5 A village, V, is 6 km from the campsite, C, and on a bearing of 220° from C. A town, T, is 8 km from C and on a bearing of 020° from C.
   (a) Make a scale drawing showing the positions of C, V and T. Use a scale of 1 cm to represent 1 km.
   (b) Find the bearing of V from T.
   (c) Find the bearing of T from V.

When Kelly looks at her initial, K, through a magnifying glass, she sees a letter K which is bigger than the real one.

The magnifying glass **enlarges** the letter K.

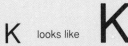   looks like   K

In this case the lengths of the lines making up the letter K have been **doubled** or **multiplied by 2**.

What Kelly sees is
an enlargement of scale factor 2.

1 ▶ Do Worksheet 8.

As well as having a scale factor, every enlargement also has a **centre**.

This is an enlargement of the triangle ABC, with scale factor 2 and centre at point X.

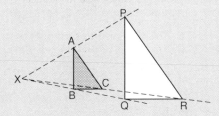

The enlarged triangle has been labelled PQR.

In the diagram
   the distance XP = 2 times the distance XA
      or XP = 2XA
and
        XQ = 2XB
and
        XR = 2XC

2 This is a triangle ABC and a point X.

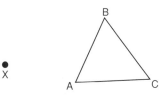

XA = 2 cm, XB = 3 cm and XC = 4 cm.

(a) Make an accurate drawing of the triangle.

(b) Draw enlargements of the triangle, centre X, of scale factors: 2, 3, 5, 6

You need graph or squared paper.

3

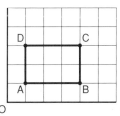

(a) Copy the rectangle onto squared or graph paper.

(b) Draw an enlargement, scale factor 3, centre O, of the rectangle.

4 (a) On squared or graph paper, plot the points
A(2, 1) B(5, 1) and C(5, 3)
and draw the triangle ABC.

(b) Draw the triangle LMN which is an enlargement of ABC, scale factor 2, centre the origin.

5 (a) Plot the points
(2, 2) (3, 3) (4, 4) (5, 3) and (6, 2)

(b) Show that it is possible to join them up to create a capital A.

(c) The letter A is enlarged by scale factor 3, centre (1, 1)
Draw the enlarged letter A.

6

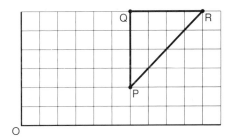

The triangle PQR is the enlargement, scale factor 2, centred on the origin, of a triangle ABC.
Find the coordinates of A, B and C.

Lesley and Peter have been learning about drawing shapes on a computer screen using LOGO.

The instructions
[fd 100 rt 90 fd 200 rt 90 fd 100 rt 90 fd 200 rt 90]
create a rectangle like this.

200
100

They make the turtle move like this:
forwards 100 units then turn 90° clockwise

forwards 200 units then turn 90° clockwise

forwards 100 units then turn 90° clockwise

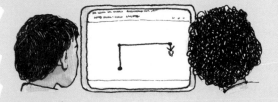

and finally forwards 200 units and a last 90° turn.

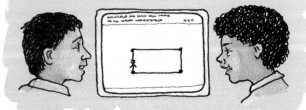

1 Write a LOGO procedure to create each of these rectangles.

(a) 100 / 50
(b) 60 / 100
(c) 180 / 200

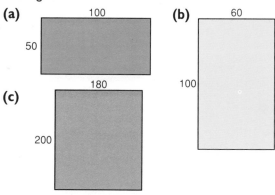

2 Write a LOGO procedure to create a square of side 100

You need access to a computer.

3 This is an equilateral triangle.
Its interior angles are all 60°
Its exterior angles are all 120°
Show that the procedure
repeat 3 **[fd 100 rt 120]**
creates an equilateral
triangle of side 100 units.

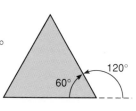

4 Write a LOGO procedure to create equilateral triangles with sides:
(a) 50 units   **(b)** 150 units
Test your procedures on a computer.

5 The exterior angle of a regular pentagon is 72°
Use your computer to show that the procedure
repeat 5 **[fd 120 rt 72]**
creates a regular pentagon with side 120 units.

6 Work out the exterior angle of a regular hexagon.
Write a LOGO procedure to draw a regular hexagon with side 100 units.
Use your computer to draw the hexagon.

7 This LOGO procedure will draw squares of various sizes.

```
squareanysize :side
repeat 4 [fd :side rt 90]
end
```

Use your computer to draw squares of different sides.

Kelly's friend Lara has another magnifying glass, but hers is an unusual one.

When she looks at her initial L what she sees is an **upside down and back to front L**

She sees an image of

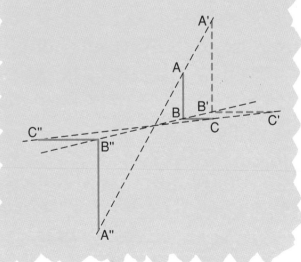

L   as

Again, the lengths in the image are double those in the original L.

Lara's magnifying glass produces
a **negative enlargement, scale factor 2**
or
an enlargement, scale factor ⁻2.

This diagram shows you how to construct an enlargement, scale factor ⁻2.

1 ▶ Do Worksheet 9.

You need squared or graph paper.

2 Using a capital letter, write the initial of your first name, with these scale factors:
- ⁻2 • ⁻3 • ⁻5

3 (a) Plot the points A(1, 1), B(3, 1) and C(3, 4)
 (b) Draw the triangle ABC.
 (c) Draw the enlargement, scale factor ⁻2, centre the origin, of the triangle ABC.

4 (a) Copy this rectangle ABCD onto squared or graph paper.

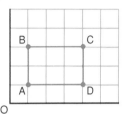

 (b) Write the coordinates of A, B, C and D.
  PQRS is the enlargement, scale factor ⁻3, centre the origin of ABCD.
 (c) Draw the rectangle PQRS.
 (d) Write the coordinates of P, Q, R and S.

5 (a) Plot the points A(1, 2) B(3, 5) and C(4, 7) on squared or graph paper.
 (b) The triangle ABC is enlarged by scale factor ⁻2 about the origin to give the triangle LMN. Find the coordinates of L, M and N.

6

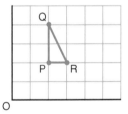

The triangle PQR is enlarged by scale factor ⁻3, centre (1, 1), to give an image EFG.
Find the coordinates of E, F and G.

7 The triangle PQR has its vertices at the points P (⁻3, ⁻3), Q (⁻6, ⁻9) and R (⁻12, ⁻6)
PQR is the enlargement, scale factor ⁻3, centre the origin of triangle ABC.
Find the coordinates of A, B and C.

8 (a) Draw the triangle ABC with vertices at the points A(2, ⁻1), B(⁻2, 4), C(3, 1)
 (b) ABC is enlarged by scale factor ⁻2, centre the origin, to give a triangle PQR. Draw the triangle PQR.
 (c) Write the coordinates of P, Q and R.

Getting the angle

Jim has an arrow head.
He lays it on the table pointing to the right.

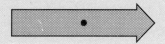

Then he rotates it about its centre through 180°
so that it is pointing to the left.

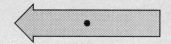

1 He always starts with the arrow head pointing to the
right. Draw the position of the arrow head when he
rotates it through an angle of:

(a) 90° anti-clockwise   (b) 90° clockwise
(c) 270° clockwise   (d) 360°
(e) 270° anti-clockwise   (f) 540° anti-clockwise.

Next Jim draws a triangle and lays
his arrow head on its base pointing
to the right.

He slides the arrow head into the
bottom left hand corner. Then he
rotates it anti-clockwise through
the angle.

He slides it along the side to the
top corner.

At the top corner he again rotates
the arrow head through this angle.

Then he slides it to the bottom
right-hand corner and rotates
it again.

Finally he slides it back to the place
where he started.

The arrow head now faces to the left.
It has been rotated through 180°.

You need to make a small arrow head from card.

2 Draw three triangles.
  • In each case start by placing the arrow head on one
    of the sides.
  • Repeat Jim's exercise.
  • Show that in each case, rotating the arrow head
    through the three angles of the triangle makes it
    finish up facing the opposite direction to the one it
    started from.

  **This confirms that the angles of a triangle
  add up to 180°.**

3 Calculate each of the angles marked x.

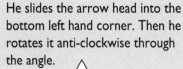

(a) x, 70°, 60°   (b) 30°, 80°, x   (c) 30°, x, 40°

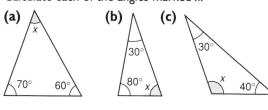

(d) 90°, 60°, x   (e) x, 55°, 45°   (f) 83°, 29°, x

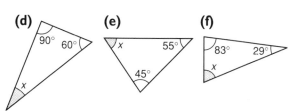

4 ABC is an isoceles triangle with BA = CA and the
angle at A = 40°. Calculate the other two angles.

As the next step, Jim drew a four-sided shape, called a **quadrilateral.**

He repeated what he had done with the triangle.

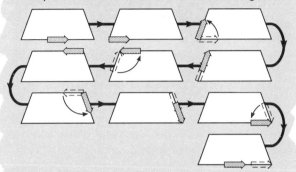

In this case his arrow head finished by pointing in the same direction as it had started.

> This means that the angles in a four-sided shape add up to 360°

5 Draw three quadrilaterals and repeat what you did for the triangles. Confirm that in each case the sum of the angles is 360°.

6 Investigate the sum of the angles for shapes with:
   (a) 5 sides **(b)** 6 sides **(c)** 7 sides.

7 Calculate the sum of the angles of:
   (a) a 10 sided shape **(b)** a 12 sided shape
   (c) a 20 sided shape **(d)** a 50 sided shape.

The sum of the interior angles inside a quadrilateral is 360°
A square is a **regular quadrilateral**, that is, one whose sides are all equal and whose angles are all equal.

To calculate the interior angle of a square

Sum of the angles = 360°
There are 4 equal angles.
Each angle is 360 ÷ 4 = 90°

8 Calculate the interior angle of:
   (a) a regular pentagon (5 sides)
   (b) a regular hexagon (6 sides)
   (c) a regular octagon (8 sides)

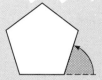

The diagram shows a pentagon.
The shaded angle is called an **exterior angle**.

9 Draw a pentagon.
   Show by using an arrow head, or by any other method, that the sum of the exterior angles of a pentagon is 360°.

10 Draw a triangle.
   Show that the sum of the exterior angles is again 360°.

> **The sum of the exterior angles of any two dimensional shape is always 360°**

11 **Investigate** a range of 2D shapes and show that in each case the sum of the exterior angles is 360°

12 Calculate the exterior angle of:
   (a) a regular hexagon
   (b) a regular pentagon
   (c) a regular octagon.

13 The diagram shows the exterior angle of a regular shape.

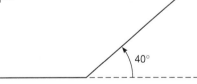

Calculate the number of sides of the shape.

14 Calculate the number of sides of a regular shape when the exterior angle is:
   (a) 36° **(b)** 72° **(c)** 45°

15 This is part of a regular shape.

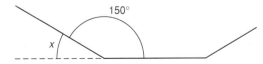

The interior angle is 150°, calculate:
   (a) the exterior angle, marked x
   (b) the number of sides of the shape.

Jenny plays a game in which she sets out on a simple journey.

On her journey she sets out from a spot marked O.
She walks 6 paces north and turns through 90° clockwise.
Then she walks 4 paces east and turns 90° clockwise.
She walks a further 3 paces before making another clockwise turn of 90°
She keeps repeating her movements and finds that she eventually gets back to the place where she started.

She describes her journey as a **(6, 4, 3)** journey.

You need squared paper.

1 Describe each of these journeys in the way Jenny has done:
   (a) 4 paces north, 3 paces east and 2 paces south
   (b) 5 paces north, 5 paces east and 4 paces south
   (c) 6 paces north, 6 paces east and 6 paces south
   (d) 8 paces north, 3 paces east and 4 paces south.
   (e) 4 paces north, 3 paces west and 5 paces south
   (f) 6 paces south, 5 paces east and 3 paces north.

2 Draw diagrams of each of the following journeys:
   (a) (6, 4, 2)   **(b)** (5, 3, 7)   **(c)** (2, 1, 4)
   (d) (7, 3, 4)   **(e)** (2, 3, 4)   **(f)** (5, 5, 1)

3 Make up three journeys of your own.
   Draw diagrams for each journey.

4 Draw diagrams for each of the following journeys:
   (a) (5, 5, 5)   **(b)** (2, 2, 1, 4)   **(c)** (⁻3, 4, 5)
   (d) (1, 1, 1, 1)   **(e)** (3, 1, 2, 4)   **(f)** (5, ⁻1, ⁻2, 3)
   Comment on each of your diagrams.

Jenny has learnt something about LOGO. She knows that she can use her computer to draw her (6, 4, 3) journey using the LOGO procedure.
   repeat 10 [fd 6 rt 90 fd 4 rt 90 fd 3 rt 90]
This will create a small picture on her computer screen.
She can create a bigger picture by multiplying the number of paces by 10 like this:
   repeat 10 [fd 60 rt 90 fd 40 rt 90 fd 30 rt 90]

You need access to a computer.
Ask your teacher for help.

5 Ask your teacher to set a computer up in LOGO.
   Write the procedure
   repeat 10 [fd 60 rt 90 fd 40 rt 90 fd 30 rt 90]
   Confirm that the procedure creates a pattern like Jenny's (6, 4, 3) journey.

The four most basic LOGO commands are:
   • fd which moves the turtle forwards
   so fd 60 moves the turtle 60 places forward.
   • **bk 50 moves the turtle 50 places back**
   • **rt 90 turns the turtle through 90° clockwise**
   • **lt 90 turns the turtle through 90° anti-clockwise.**

6 Write a LOGO procedure for each of these journeys:
   (a) (6, 4, 2)   **(b)** (5, 4, 3)   **(c)** (6, 3, 1)
   (d) (2, 3, 5)   **(e)** (4, 4, 2, 1)   **(f)** (1, 3, 4, 5)
   Use your computer, with a sufficiently large scale for the units moved, to create the patterns of the journeys. Copy each journey onto squared paper.

7 Write a LOGO procedure for each of these journeys:
   (a) (⁻2, 5, 4)   **(b)** (3, ⁻4, 5)   **(c)** (⁻1, ⁻2, 4)
   Use your computer, with a sufficiently large scale for the units moved, to create the patterns of the journeys. Copy each journey onto squared paper.

8 Use your computer to examine the following LOGO procedures:
   (a) repeat 10 **[fd 50 rt 120]**
   (b) repeat 1000 **[fd 100 rt 179]**
   Comment, with reasons, on the pictures shown on the computer screen.

Tessa has a box of flat shapes.

She takes out a collection of squares all the same size. She can cover the space on her table without leaving any gaps by placing the squares side by side.

She can do it like this

or like this

When she can do this, the shape (a square in this case) is said to
> **tessellate the plane of Tessa's table top**
or
> **tessellate the plane**
or
> **tessellate two dimensional space.**

You need some flat shapes.

1 Show that:
  (a) a set of equal sized equilateral triangles tessellates the plane
  (b) a set of equal sized regular hexagons tessellates the plane
  (c) a set of equal sized regular octagons does not tessellate the plane.

2 Show that it is possible to tessellate the plane using a set of regular octagons and small squares.

3 Decide whether any set of equal sized parallelograms will or will not tessellate the plane.

Tessa knows that there is a simple way of deciding whether or not a shape tessellates the plane.

The angles at a point add up to 360°

The angle at each corner of a square is 90°

So, when Tessa fits four squares together, she gets
  4 lots of 90 or $4 \times 90 = 360°$
which is the angle at a point.
There will be no gaps. The space has been filled.

> Any regular shape tessellates the plane if the angle at a corner of that shape can be divided exactly into 360.

To show that a regular hexagon **will** tessellate the plane:

The angle at a corner of a regular hexagon is 120°
  $360 \div 120 = 3$ exactly
so a regular hexagon will tessellate the plane.

To show that a regular octagon **will not** tessellate the plane:

The angle at a corner of a regular octagon is 135°
  $360 \div 135 = 2.666$ not a whole number
so a regular octagon will not tessellate the plane.

4 **(a)** Calculate the angle at a corner of a regular nine sided shape.
  (b) Decide whether or not a set of equal sized nine sided shapes will tessellate the plane.

5 A set of equal sized isosceles triangles have their angles as 70°, 70° and 40°.
  Decide whether or not such a set of triangles will tessellate the plane.

▶ **Investigation**

6 **Investigate** your set of shapes. Decide which will and which will not tessellate the plane. Record your results.

Probably a winner

Class 11Y at Audley High School are choosing a person to sit on the School Council.
They decide to do it by putting the names of five people in a hat and drawing one name out at random.
The names of the five people are

Sharon   Andy   Penny   Trish   Roy

One name is pulled out of the hat.
The probability of any one of the names being pulled out of the hat is

$\frac{1}{5}$ or   **0·2** (in decimals)   or   **20%** (in percentages)

This can be written as
probability of Sharon being chosen = $\frac{1}{5}$ or 0·2 or 20%
or **p(Sharon)** = $\frac{1}{5}$ or **0·2** or **20%**

and

p(Andy)   = $\frac{1}{5}$ or 0·2 or 20%

p(Penny)   = $\frac{1}{5}$ or 0·2 or 20%

p(Trish)   = $\frac{1}{5}$ or 0·2 or 20%

p(Roy)   = $\frac{1}{5}$ or 0·2 or 20%

The sum of these probabilities is

$\frac{1}{5} + \frac{1}{5} + \frac{1}{5} + \frac{1}{5} + \frac{1}{5} = 1$

or 0·2 + 0·2 + 0·2 + 0·2 + 0·2 = 1

or 20% + 20% + 20% + 20% + 20% = 100%

The sum of the probabilities of all the possible outcomes of any event is always 1 (or 100%)

The probability of Sharon **not** being chosen is
$\frac{4}{5}$ or **0·8** or **80%**

The probability of something *not* happening is always 1 minus the probability of it happening or 100 minus the probability of it happening if you use percentages.

Probability should always be given as a fraction, decimal or percentage and nothing else.

Mr Yeats, the class teacher, is responsible for putting the names in the hat. He is well-known for his ability to make mistakes. This time he writes two slips of paper with Sharon's name on it, one with Andy's name, one with Penny's name, one with Trish's name and none with Roy's name.

1 **(a)** Write down, as a fraction, the probability that the person chosen will be:
   • Sharon   • Andy   • Penny   • Trish   • Roy.
   (b) Show that the sum of these probabilities is 1

2 Re-write all of the probabilities in question 1 as:
   (a) decimals   **(b)** percentages.

3 Show that:
   (a) the sum of the decimals in question **2(a)** is 1
   (b) the sum of the percentages in question **2(b)** is 100%

4 Write the probability that Sharon will not be chosen:
   (a) as a fraction   **(b)** as a decimal
   (c) as a percentage.

5 Write, as a percentage, the probability that Roy will not be chosen.

Audley High School organise a raffle. They sell 500 tickets labelled from number 1 to number 500. One ticket is selected at random as the winner. Class 11Y buy 40 tickets and Mr Yeats buys 10 tickets.

---

6 **(a)** Work out the probability that class 11Y will have the winning ticket. Give your answer as:
   • a fraction   • a decimal   • a percentage.
   (b) Write the fraction for **(a)** in its lowest terms.
   (c) Work out the probability that class 11Y will not have the winning ticket.

7 Work out the probability that Mr Yeats will:
   (a) have the winning ticket
   (b) not have the winning ticket.

   Give your answers in any one form.

8 What is the probability that the raffle will be won by either class 11Y or their teacher, Mr Yeats?

9 What is the probability that the raffle will be won by neither class 11Y nor their teacher?

There are 30 students in class 11Y. 16 are girls and 14 are boys.

They put all their names in a hat to select the first person to use the new computer. This time Mr Yeats makes no mistakes. One name is selected at random.

10 What is the probability:
(a) that it will be Sharon's name that is chosen
(b) that it will not be Sharon who is chosen
(c) that it will be:
  • a girl's name that is chosen
  • a boy's name that is chosen?
You may write your answer as a fraction, decimal or percentage.

At the school fair class 11Y organise a game of chance. Twenty coloured balls are placed in a hat.
Ten of these balls are red, four are blue, three are green, two are yellow and one is white.

Select a ball at RANDOM
10p a go!
Red ball loses.
Any other colour wins a prize.
White ball wins JACKPOT PRIZE

11 Mr Yeats pays 10p to have a go.
What is the probability of Mr Yeats:
(a) winning a prize
(b) selecting a blue ball
(c) not winning a prize
(d) selecting a ball that is not blue
(e) selecting a ball that is not yellow
(f) selecting a black ball
(g) winning the jackpot prize
(h) not winning the jackpot prize.

12 Mrs Yeats pays 20p so that she can have two tries.
What is the probability that Mrs Yeats will select:
(a) a red ball   (b) a ball that is not green.

Mr Yeats organises the students into six groups, with 4 or 5 in each group. This is to help decide which group will run the stall at the summer fair at various times of the day. They are Group 1, Group 2, Group 3, Group 4, Group 5 and Group 6

To decide which group runs the stall first he rolls a die. The group that starts is the group whose number shows on the die.

13 What is the probability that:
(a) Group 2 will start
(b) Group 2 will not start
(c) Group 6 will not start
(d) the group that starts is an even numbered group
(e) the group that starts is an odd numbered group
(f) the group that starts is a prime numbered group
(g) the group that starts is not a prime numbered group
(h) the group that starts is either Group 2 or Group 3
(i) it is neither Group 2 nor Group 3 which starts
(j) it is none of Groups 1, 2, 3 or 4 that starts?

Mr Yeats is very good at inventing games of chance. One day he gives class 11Y a problem about a new game. In one hat he has slips of paper which have each of the numbers from 1 to 50 written on them, one number per slip of paper.
In another hat he has slips of paper, each one of which has a letter of the alphabet written on it. All the letters are used.

He asks Trish to select a slip of paper from the first hat. He asks Roy to select a slip of paper from the second hat.

Trish will win a prize if her slip of paper has a **prime number** written on it.
Roy will win a prize if his slip of paper has a **vowel** written on it.

14 What is the probability that:
(a) Trish will win a prize
(b) Roy will win a prize
(c) Trish will not win a prize
(d) Roy will not win a prize?

15 Who, out of Trish and Roy, has the best chance of winning a prize? Explain your answer.

Making the connection

● **Remember**

Scatter diagrams can be used to show whether there is a connection between two sets of data.

The two sets of data **must** be **numbers** like
weight
age
year
height
size of collar

The connection between two sets of data is called correlation.

There can be different types of correlation.

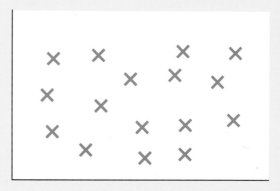

In this scatter graph there is no correlation. The points are just randomly and widely spread about. This is evidence of **no correlation** or **zero correlation**.

In this scatter graph the points slope upwards and there is **good correlation** and **positive correlation.**

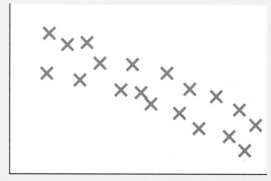

In this scatter graph the points slope downwards and there is **inverse correlation** or **negative correlation**. One set of results increases whilst the other decreases.

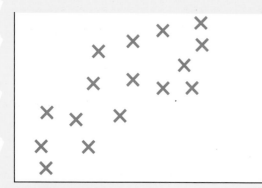

In this scatter graph the points again slope upwards but there is greater spread amongst them. In this case there is evidence of **some positive correlation**, but it is **not very good**.

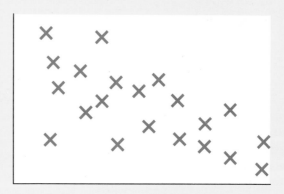

In this scatter graph there is **some negative correlation** as the points generally slope downwards but they are spread about.

1 The height and shoe sizes of ten people are shown below.

Height (cm)	159	173	159	165	151	162	156	161	167	176
Shoe size	6	9	4	8	3	7	5	8	10	11

(a) Draw a scatter graph for this information.

(b) Comment on the correlation.

2 The length and width of twelve leaves from a tree were measured and recorded in the table below.

Length (cm)	66	89	63	68	87	80	89	61	73	77	85	91
Width (cm)	35	41	27	35	39	40	39	35	37	39	41	44

(a) Draw a scatter diagram for this data.

(b) Comment on the correlation.

3 The mathematics and science percentages gained by 13 students in an examination are shown in the table below.

Maths	61	79	34	68	45	56	83	72	93	88	51	39	77
Science	65	74	29	75	39	51	85	72	88	91	56	36	78

(a) Draw a scatter graph for this data.

(b) Comment on the correlation.

4 The size of engine and miles per gallon were recorded for twelve cars.

Engine size (cc)	1600	2000	2000	900	1200	1800
Miles per gallon	38	38	36	52	48	40
Engine size (cc)	1000	3500	1600	2600	1300	1900
Miles per gallon	46	18	42	25	49	39

(a) Draw a scatter graph for this data.

(b) Comment on the correlation.

5 Draw a scatter graph and comment on the correlation for the data about ages and weights of the nine people.

Name	Age in years	Weight in kilograms
Michael	16	65
Anne	20	46
Gulzar	15	53
Jenny	15	49
Asif	18	73
Imran	17	91
Katrina	22	56
Asha	14	63
Lenny	17	105

6 Say, with your reasons, whether you think there is

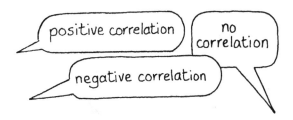

for each of the following:

(a) number of cars and adults in a family

(b) size of a house and number of bathrooms in it

(c) the height and weight of people

(d) the speed of a train and the time for a journey

(e) the shoe size of people and the amount they earn

(f) the number of rooms in a house and the number of doors in it

(g) the number of ice creams sold and the time of year

(h) the age of a woman and the number of children she has given birth to

(i) the number of telephone calls made and the time of day

(j) the age of a man and the number of hours of sleep he has

(k) the cost of a newspaper and the number of pages in it

(l) the number of goals scored by a professional football team and the average attendance at home matches

(m) the price of a holiday and the distance from Belfast to a holiday resort

(n) the cost of a new car and the size of its engine

(o) the number of people in a family and the amount they spend on food each week

(p) the life expectancy of a person and the number of cigarettes they smoke each day

(q) the distance someone travels to school, college or work and the amount of food they eat each day.

7 Carry out a survey to find out whether there is a relationship between two sets of data.

Support your comments on the relationship by using scatter graphs.

Some ideas are:

- marks in English and Geography or any two subjects
- ages and heights
- heights and weights
- distances travelled to school and times of arrival.

From one to the other

Katarina and her family are touring England, Scotland and Wales for their summer holiday. Their home is in Germany.

In Germany all distances are measured in kilometres.
Distances in Britain are measured in miles. This can be very confusing.

To help her family, Katarina has made a graph which converts miles to kilometres and vice versa.

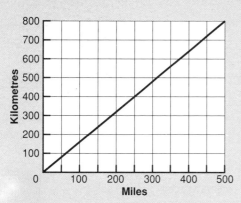

It shows that **500 miles is the same as 800 kilometres**.

1 Copy the graph and use it to convert:
   (a) 200 miles to kilometres
   (b) 320 miles to kilometres
   (c) 400 kilometres to miles
   (d) 150 kilometres to miles
   (e) 455 miles to kilometres
   (f) 560 kilometres to miles.

2 Maggie, who lives in Dublin, has arranged to meet her friend Katarina in Liverpool.

For her visit to Liverpool Maggie changes her Irish money to British money.
The graph below is a conversion graph which shows how to change between Irish and British money.

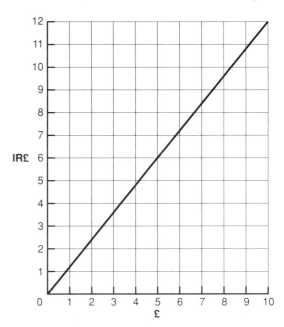

Copy the graph and use it to convert:
(a) IR£6 to £   (b) IR£120 to £   (c) IR£30 to £
(d) £5 to IR£   (e) £20 to IR£   (f) £65 to IR£

3 Maggie has saved IR£150 for her trip. How much is this worth in British money?

4 At the end of her trip Maggie has £27 left. She changes this back to Irish money. How much will she receive?

These are extracts from the pages of three different books.

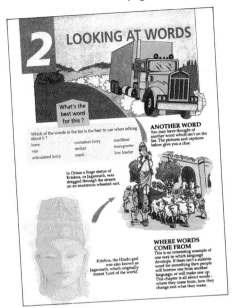

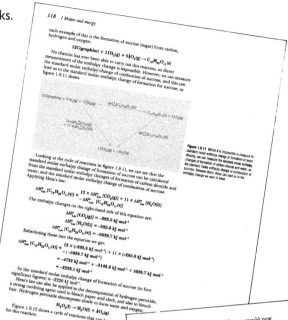

You can work on this topic with a friend or in a small group.

You need three different types of book from the school library, your teacher or your home.

In this topic you are going to make an analysis of the text and style of the books you have collected.

In your analysis look at a range of ideas. Here are some you could consider:

* the amount of space for pictures
* the number of pages in the books
* the size of the print
* the average word length on a page
* the use of colour
* the number of words on a page
* the average number of words in a sentence
* the age of reader for whom the book is suitable
* the number of chapters
* the number of paragraphs
* if it is a library book, how popular the book is with readers.

You can also consider any ideas of your own choice.

It is important to state clearly which ideas you are going to examine, giving the reasons for your choice. Discuss these ideas with your teacher.

Present the results of your findings in as clear a way as possible.

What conclusions can you make from your analysis?

Explain your reasons behind these conclusions.

Pose some questions that other people might consider if they wanted to make an analysis of the books or type of books you have chosen.

Lucy has written a programme for her computer in LOGO. It produces a regular hexagon on the screen.

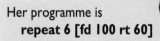

Her programme is
repeat 6 [fd 100 rt 60]

What this does is quite straightforward.

repeat 6 tells the computer to do the same thing 6 times

fd 100 tells the computer to go 100 places forward in the direction it is pointing

rt 60 tells the computer that after moving 100 places forward, the turtle must turn through 60° in the clockwise direction.

So the **repeat 6** instruction tells the turtle to move the 100 places followed by the 60° turn 6 times.

This now produces the regular hexagon for Lucy.

You need a computer set up for LOGO.

1 Try to explain why the programme produces a hexagon for Lucy.

2 Keep the **repeat, fd** and **rt** instructions in the programme but **investigate** the shapes and patterns that can be drawn by changing the value of 6, 100 and 60 in the programme.

As well as **fd** and **rt** LOGO also has the instructions
bk 100 which will move the turtle 100 places backwards and
lt 80 which will turn the turtle through 80° anti-clockwise

3 Enter the following LOGO programme into your computer
repeat 4 [bk 60 lt 90]
What shape does this produce?
Explain why it produces such a shape.

4 Keep the **repeat, bk** and **lt** instructions but again vary the numerical values in the above programme.
Investigate the shapes and patterns produced.
Record and explain any results.

5 Enter the following LOGO programme into your computer
repeat 4 [fd 100 rt 90 fd 60 rt 90 fd 20 rt 90]
Copy the shape or pattern produced by the computer onto paper.
Comment, as fully as possible, on this shape or pattern.
Try to give some explanation.

6 Repeat what you have done in question **5** but use the LOGO programme.
repeat 4
[fd 80 rt 90 fd 40 rt 90 fd 40 rt 90 fd 20 rt 90]
Copy the shape or pattern onto paper.
Comment on the shape or pattern.

7 What do you think will happen to the shape or pattern if the **4** which follows **repeat** is changed to some other number?

8 Using **repeat, fd, bk, lt** and **rt**, write some LOGO programmes of your own.
In each case vary the numerical values and copy the shapes or patterns onto paper.
Comment on each of these shapes or patterns.
Investigate these shapes or patterns as fully as possible.

9 Enter the following LOGO programme into your computer
repeat 10
[fd 10] rt 90 repeat 10 [fd 10] rt 135 fd 141
Copy the shape produced onto paper.
Comment as fully as possible on this shape.

10 Write your own LOGO programme similar to the one in question **9**.
You should keep the same instructions but vary the numerical values.
Copy the various shapes or patterns produced by the computer onto paper.
Investigate this situation as fully as possible.

11 Write any and as many LOGO programmes of your own choice as you wish.
Copy the various shapes or patterns produced by the computer onto paper.
Comment as fully as possible on these shapes or patterns.

Squares have been drawn on the sides of three triangles.

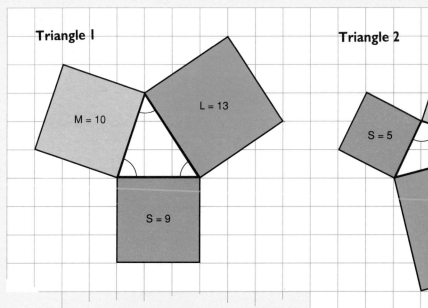

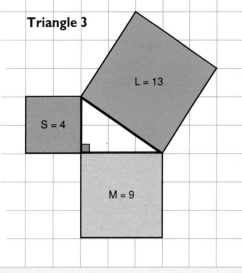

In Triangle 1 all the angles are acute.
In Triangle 2 one of the angles is obtuse.
In Triangle 3 one of the angles is a right angle.

Each triangle has a large square, **L**,
a middle sized square, **M**,
and a small square, **S**.

The areas of the squares are given in the table below.

	Large	Middle	Small
Triangle 1	13	10	9
Triangle 2	17	10	5
Triangle 3	13	9	4

1 Check that the areas in the table are correct.
Show your working.

You need squared paper.

2 (a) Draw three triangles which have:
   • all acute angles
   • an obtuse angle
   • a right-angle.

(b) Draw the squares on all of the sides of each triangle.

(c) Find the area of each square.

(d) Record your results.
In some cases **L < S + M**,
in some cases **L > S + M** and
in some cases **L = S + M**

Investigate these three cases for L, M and S.
Record your conclusions and general
statements.
Test your conclusions and general statements.

A famous number sequence

When we write

2^3 it is called the **second cube number**

it means $2 \times 2 \times 2 = 8$

When we write

4^2 it is called the **fourth square number**

it means $4 \times 4 = 16$

So $1^3 + 2^3 + 3^3 + 4^3$ is called the sum of the **first four cube numbers** and means

$$1 \times 1 \times 1 + 2 \times 2 \times 2 + 3 \times 3 \times 3 + 4 \times 4 \times 4$$
$$= \quad 1 \quad + \quad 8 \quad + \quad 27 \quad + \quad 64$$
$$= \quad\quad 9 \quad\quad + \quad 27 \quad + \quad 64$$
$$= \quad\quad\quad 36 \quad\quad\quad + \quad 64$$
$$= \quad\quad\quad\quad 100$$
$$= \quad\quad\quad\quad 10^2 \quad \text{which is the \textbf{tenth square number}}$$

So
1 + 2 + 3 + 4 = 10

and
$1^3 + 2^3 + 3^3 + 4^3 = 10^2$

The aim of this investigation is to examine this result and see if this result is merely a fluke or can be generalised.

1 Work out
$$1^3 + 2^3 + 3^3 + 4^3 + 5^3$$
and check to see if it is equal to
$$(1 + 2 + 3 + 4 + 5)^2$$
That is, does it equal
$$15^2?$$

2 Work out the sum of the first six cube numbers.
Does it equal $(1 + 2 + 3 + 4 + 5 + 6)^2$?

3 **Investigate** the relationship between the sum of the first collection of cube numbers and the square numbers.

Show all of your working.
Record your results and observations.
Give and test any general results.